The Financial
PLANNING
WORKBOOK

A Comprehensive Guide to Building a
Successful Financial Plan

ISBN: 1733591117
ISBN-13: 978-1733591119

CONTENTS

CHAPTER 1

———•—

Preparing Your Financial Plan

Welcome to *The Financial Planning Workbook*. Our goal is to help you build or repair your financial plan using the proven methods and exercises outlined in the following chapters. Inside this book you will be introduced to the practice of personal financial planning and you will learn how to create and monitor a successful financial plan. But before you can begin your path to financial independence, you first need to identify your starting point. By recognizing where you are today, you'll be able to set tangible goals and track your success from this point forward.

Exercise 1.1: Identifying Your Habits

For this exercise, place a check mark next to the statements that apply to you. The chapters that follow will help you break these poor financial habits and replace them with responsible alternatives.

_____ I routinely carry a balance on my credit cards that I'm unable to pay in full each month.

_____ At least one of my credit cards is currently maxed out.

_____ I've had to borrow money from family or friends to pay my bills within the last year.

_____ I do not have any money saved for emergencies.

_____ I don't bother balancing my checkbook or reconciling my bank statements at the end of each month.

_____ I'm not sure whether my employer offers a retirement plan or a company match.

_____ I'm not sure how much I'm currently saving towards retirement.

_____ I haven't reviewed my investments within the last year.

_____ I don't have a will, living will, financial power of attorney, or healthcare power of attorney.

_____ I haven't given serious thought to when I'd like to retire or how much I plan to spend during retirement.

_____ I'm not sure what would happen if I became disabled and couldn't pay my bills.

_____ I'm not sure if my family would be financially stable if I were to die.

Exercise 1.2: Evaluating Your Current Financial Plan

Now that you've identified the parts of your financial plan that may be failing you, it's time to assess your strengths. Place a check mark below to indicate whether the statement on the left is satisfactory or needs further improvement.

	Satisfactory	Needs Improvement
My ability to set realistic and attainable financial goals	_____	_____
My ability to create and maintain a budget	_____	_____
My ability to save money	_____	_____
My credit score	_____	_____
My understanding of the investments I have and their associated risks	_____	_____
My current level of retirement savings	_____	_____
Life and disability insurance premiums, deductibles, and coverage amounts	_____	_____
Home, auto, and umbrella insurance premiums, deductibles, and coverage amounts	_____	_____
My overall estate plan	_____	_____

Exercise 1.3: How Well Do You Know Your Financial Situation?

Maybe you've identified a few bad habits that you'd like to break and you realize that a fair amount of your financial plan needs improvement. It's unlikely that you've intentionally made poor financial decisions that led you to this point; it's much more likely your financial plan has been failing you because you simply aren't aware of the many intricate details involved. To explore this possibility, select which of the following statements are true and false regarding your present financial situation.

T ❑   F ❑   I know how much I earn and how much I spend each month, and what my savings surplus or deficit is.

T ❑   F ❑   I know the value of my assets, liabilities, and net worth within a few thousand dollars.

T ❑   F ❑   I have recently reviewed the various lines of insurance that I have and discussed their adequacy with my insurance agent.

T ❑   F ❑   I have met with my accountant to discuss tax planning strategies within the last year.

T ❑   F ❑   I understand the basic characteristics of the various investments that I own and they match my tolerance for risk.

T ❑   F ❑   I know how each of my investments has performed over the last year.

T ❑   F ❑   I know the fees associated with each of my investments.

T ❑   F ❑   I know the current balance of my investment accounts within a few thousand dollars.

T ❑   F ❑   I participate in my employer's retirement plan and take advantage of the company match.

T ❑   F ❑   I make the maximum contribution to my IRA each year.

T ❑   F ❑   I have reviewed my credit report and checked my credit score within the last year.

T ❑   F ❑   I know how much state and federal estate tax would be payable if I were to die this year.

T ❑   F ❑   I have recently reviewed my estate plan with an attorney.

Now that you have a strong understanding of your overall strengths and weaknesses, write down three aspects of your financial plan that you'd like to improve over the next year:

1. _____

2. _____

3. _____

If you were to improve the three aspects that you wrote down, how would it make you feel? One year from now, if you were on track to meet your retirement goal, had the proper lines of insurance in place to protect your family, and were on the path to becoming debt free, what would that mean to you and your family?

_____

_____

_____

_____

_____

Exercise 1.4: Identifying Your Financial Concerns

Each chapter of this workbook will guide you through a different aspect of your financial plan. You'll learn that each topic carries its own set of obstacles and challenges that you'll need to overcome. In this exercise, you'll begin to learn what those challenges will be by identifying what you're afraid of when it comes to your financial future. Place a check mark next to the following items that worry you.

_____   Low investment returns

_____   Losing my job

_____   Another "Great Recession"

_____   High inflation

_____   Rising taxes

_____   Social Security cuts

_____   Rising medical costs

_____   Outliving my money

Exercise 1.5: Gathering Data

Throughout this workbook you'll be asked to call upon various financial documents that will be used to build your financial plan. The National Association of Personal Financial Advisors (NAPFA) provides the following list of documents that you should gather. For this exercise, locate each of the following documents and record their current storage location in the space provided.

Documents	Storage Location
Bank records	
Birth certificate	
Credit card statements	
Debt statements	
Estate planning documents	
Insurance policies	
Investment account statements	
Marriage license	
Military records	
Retirement account statements	
Tax returns	
Titles and deeds to property	

Where to locate missing information:
- ✓ Banks, insurance providers, and brokerage houses
- ✓ Computer recycle bin
- ✓ County auditor's office
- ✓ Credit bureaus
- ✓ Digital cloud storage
- ✓ Glove compartment in car
- ✓ Off-site storage unit
- ✓ Online public records
- ✓ Parents, siblings, and other family members

Exercise 1.6: Complete Your Personal Summaries

The summaries that follow are critical to keeping you organized as you build your financial plan. Through careful organization you'll be able to continue to the next steps of the financial planning process, which are analyzing your data and setting goals. Revisit these summaries every six months or any time you experience a major life event, such as marriage, divorce, birth of a child, death of a family member, or job change.

Personal Information

	You	Spouse/Partner
Name:	_____	_____
Home address:	_____	_____
Country of residence:	_____	_____
Marital status:	_____	_____
Maiden name:	_____	_____
Date of birth:	_____	_____
Social Security number:	_____	_____
Driver's license number:	_____	_____
Driver's license state of issue:	_____	_____
Driver's license expiration:	_____	_____
Home phone:	_____	_____
Cell phone:	_____	_____
Home fax:	_____	_____
Email 1:	_____	_____
Email 2:	_____	_____

Employment Information

	You	**Spouse/Partner**
Employer:	_____	_____
Job title:	_____	_____
Office address:	_____	_____
Office phone:	_____	_____
Office fax:	_____	_____
Start date:	_____	_____
Salary:	_____	_____

Advisor Information

	Advisor 1	**Advisor 2**
Name:	_____	_____
Profession:	_____	_____
Employer:	_____	_____
Office address:	_____	_____
Office phone:	_____	_____
Cell phone:	_____	_____
Office fax:	_____	_____
Email:	_____	_____
Fee:	_____	_____

	Advisor 3	**Advisor 4**
Name:	_____	_____
Profession:	_____	_____

Employer: _____ _____

Office address: _____ _____

Office phone: _____ _____

Cell phone: _____ _____

Office fax: _____ _____

Email: _____ _____

Fee: _____ _____

Exercise 1.7: Setting Goals

In this exercise you will begin setting goals for yourself and your family. First think in broad terms, such as what you would do if you weren't burdened by your full-time job and routine financial responsibilities. Then you'll set detailed, tangible goals using the templates provided, and finally you'll create a short-term action plan to accomplish your most important goal.

Write down what you would do if you received a check for $5 million today.

_____

_____

_____

_____

With $5 million, who could you help and what positive impact could you have on your community or the causes that you care the most about?

_____

_____

_____

_____

If you were no longer required to work, how would you spend your time?

_____

_____

_____

_____

Now that you've considered your goals in general terms, it's time to get more specific. For each category listed, consider if it's a goal that you'd like to pursue. If it is, be as specific as possible by listing the year that you'd like to accomplish the goal and how much it will cost.

My Retirement Goal

Year I plan to retire: _____   Annual retirement expenses: $_____

State where I plan to live during retirement: _____

✓ *You will build a detailed retirement plan in Chapter 5.*

Travel

Destination: _____   Year: _____

Amount: $_____   How often: _____   For how many times: _____

✓ *For example, assume that you would like to travel to Hawaii (destination) in 2020 (year) and spend $5,000 (amount). You would like to return to Hawaii every 5 years (how often) for a total of 3 trips (how many times).*

New Vehicle

Description: _____   Year: _____

Amount: $_____   How often: _____   For how many times: _____

✓ *For example, assume that you would like to purchase a new car (description) in 2020 (year) and make a down payment of $4,000 (amount). You would like to purchase a new car every 8 years (how often) for a total of 3 times (how many times).*

New Home

Description: _____ Year: _____

Down payment amount: $_____

✓ *In Chapter 3 you will determine the home price that you can afford.*

Home Renovation

Description: _____ Year: _____

Amount: $_____ How often: _____ For how many times: _____

Major Purchase

Description: _____ Year: _____

Amount: $_____ How often: _____ For how many times: _____

Wedding

Name and relationship: _____

Location: _____ Year: _____ Amount: $_____

Celebration

Description: _____ Year: _____

Amount: $_____ How often: _____ For how many times: _____

Education

Name and relationship: _____

Starting year: _____ Number of years: _____ Amount: $_____

✓ *You will complete a detailed college funding analysis in Chapter 7.*

Gifts & Donations

Description: _____ Year: _____

Amount: $_____ How often: _____ For how many times: _____

Start a Business

Description: _____ Year: _____

Initial investment amount: $_____

Health Care

Description: _____ Year: _____

Amount: $_____ How often: _____ For how many times: _____

Provide Care

Name and relationship: _____ Year: _____

Amount: $_____ How often: _____ For how many times: _____

✓ *For example, assume that you would like to provide care for your mother (relationship) beginning in 2020 (year) and you estimate the cost will be $5,000 per year. You expect to provide care every year (how often) for the next 10 years (how many times).*

Leave Bequest

Description: _____ Amount: $_____

Recipient: _____

Other Goal

Description: _____ Year: _____

Amount: $_____ How often: _____ For how many times: _____

Exercise 1.8: Review Your Goals

This may be the first time that you've written down your goals and assigned dollar values and time frames to each of them. Planning for so many goals can quickly become an overwhelming experience, so it's important to prioritize them. In the fields provided, place a check mark next to each goal to indicate its time frame and then assign a priority rank. This will allow you to visualize which goals are fast approaching and which are most important to you.

	Short-Term 1 to 5 Years	Mid-Term 6 to 10 Years	Long-Term 10+ Years	Priority Rank
Retirement:	_____	_____	_____	_____
Travel:	_____	_____	_____	_____
New Vehicle:	_____	_____	_____	_____
New Home:	_____	_____	_____	_____
Home Renovation:	_____	_____	_____	_____
Major Purchase:	_____	_____	_____	_____
Wedding:	_____	_____	_____	_____
Celebration:	_____	_____	_____	_____
Education:	_____	_____	_____	_____
Gifts & Donations:	_____	_____	_____	_____
Start a Business:	_____	_____	_____	_____
Health Care:	_____	_____	_____	_____
Provide Care:	_____	_____	_____	_____
Leave Bequest:	_____	_____	_____	_____
Other Goal:	_____	_____	_____	_____

Exercise 1.9: Create Your Action Plan

Identify your highest priority goal from the previous exercise and write down the specific steps that you will take over the next four weeks to help you achieve that goal. Each month select a new goal and complete a similar summary.

My highest priority goal: _____

Week 1

Actionable step: _____

Who will hold me accountable?_____

Cost to complete this step: $_____   Date completed: _____

Week 2

Actionable step: _____

Who will hold me accountable?_____

Cost to complete this step: $_____   Date completed: _____

Week 3

Actionable step: _____

Who will hold me accountable?_____

Cost to complete this step: $_____   Date completed: _____

Week 4

Actionable step: _____

Who will hold me accountable?_____

Cost to complete this step: $_____   Date completed: _____

CHAPTER 2

---·—·---

Income Planning

You can only achieve the goals that you defined in Chapter 1 by learning how to manage your cash flow. In fact, cash flow management is the most important part of your financial plan because without it, you'll slip into debt and your plan will not succeed. Tracking your cash flow is simple and only takes a few minutes each month. You don't need to create a complicated, overly-detailed worksheet. You only need to include enough information so that you can see how much you spend and how much you earn. To begin this process, first review all of the sources of income listed in Exercise 2.1 and write down the dollar amounts attributed to those that apply to you.

Exercise 2.1: Annual Income Forecast

Job 1:	$_____	Tax refund:	$_____
Job 2:	$_____	Trust income:	$_____
Dividends:	$_____	Alimony:	$_____
Interest:	$_____	Child support:	$_____
Social Security:	$_____	Inheritance:	$_____
Pension income:	$_____	Unemployment:	$_____
Annuity income:	$_____	Other:	$_____
Rental income:	$_____	Other:	$_____

Total Annual Income: $_____

Now that you have a clear understanding of how much you earn each year, how do you compare to your peers? Throughout this workbook you'll be provided with a series of benchmarks that will allow you to identify your strengths and weaknesses. By comparing yourself to these benchmarks you will see what parts of your financial plan are in good working order and what parts need improvement.

Median Income by Education Level		
Degree	**Men's Income**	**Women's Income**
Professional degree (MD, JD)	$107,050	$63,353
Doctorate degree	$91,770	$62,388
Master's degree	$76,386	$50,255
Bachelor's degree	$60,933	$40,033

Source: CNBC

Have you ever wondered how much you would need to earn to be part of the "1% Club"? According to *Forbes*, a household income of $389,436 will rank you among the top 1% of all income earners in the US. But that is the *national average*, and the amount required to be part of the top 1% varies by location. A few examples are provided below. And if you're curious what it takes to be part of the top 0.01%? That requires an annual income of $8,320,000!

New Mexico:	$231,276	Summit Park, UT:	$1,210,000
New Jersey:	$547,737	Bridgeport, CT:	$1,390,000
Washington, D.C.:	$554,719	Jackson, WY:	$1,650,000
Connecticut:	$659,979	*National Average:*	*$389,436*

Exercise 2.2: Annual Expense Forecast

In the upcoming exercises you'll be asked to track your expenses in several different ways. First, you'll develop your budget by estimating how much you expect to spend in each of the broad categories provided. Then you'll be asked to track your *actual spending*, beginning today, over the course of the next several months. Finally, you will compare your budget with how much you actually spent to better understand your spending habits.

Automobile

Gas: $_____   Maintenance: $_____

Registration: $_____   Repairs: $_____

Accessories: $_____   Other: $_____

Total Automobile Expenses: $_____

Child Expenses

Babysitting: $_____   Child support: $_____

Allowance: $_____   Activities: $_____

Day care: $_____   Other: $_____

Total Child Expenses: $_____

Clothing

Wardrobe: $_____   Dry cleaning: $_____

Shoes: $_____   Other: $_____

Total Clothing Expenses: $_____

Consumer Debt Payments

Vehicle loans: $_____   Personal loans: $_____

Credit cards: $_____   Other: $_____

Total Consumer Debt Payments: $_____

Dining

Restaurants: $_____   Groceries: $_____

Take out: $_____   Other: $_____

Total Dining Expenses: $_____

Education

College savings: $_____   Student loans: $_____

Tuition: $_____   Self-education: $_____

Room & board: $_____   Other: $_____

Total Education Expenses: $_____

Gifts

Friends: $_____   Siblings: $_____

Parents: $_____   Charities: $_____

Spouse/partner: $_____   Other: $_____

Total Gift Expenses: $_____

Health Care

Physician: $_____   Dental: $_____

Vision: $_____   Specialist: $_____

Medication: $_____   Other: $_____

Total Health Care Expenses: $_____

Household

Furniture: $_____   Repairs: $_____

Accessories: $_____   Home security: $_____

Cleaning: $_____   Lawn care: $_____

Pets: $_____   Other: $_____

Total Household Expenses: $_____

Housing

Mortgage:	$_____	HOA fees:	$_____
Equity line:	$_____	Rent:	$_____
Vacation home:	$_____	Other:	$_____

Total Housing Expenses: $_____

Insurance

Automobile:	$_____	Health:	$_____
Homeowners:	$_____	Life:	$_____
Umbrella:	$_____	Disability:	$_____
Long-term care:	$_____	Other:	$_____

Total Insurance Expenses: $_____

Membership Dues

Health club:	$_____	Country club:	$_____
Professional:	$_____	Other:	$_____

Total Membership Dues: $_____

Professional Fees

Accountant:	$_____	Attorney:	$_____
Insurance agent:	$_____	Stock broker:	$_____
Financial advisor:	$_____	Other:	$_____

Total Professional Fees: $_____

Recreation

Hobbies: $_____   Travel: $_____

Entertainment: $_____   Other: $_____

Total Recreation Expenses: $_____

Taxes

Federal: $_____   Medicare: $_____

State: $_____   Property: $_____

Local: $_____   Capital gains: $_____

Social Security: $_____   Other: $_____

Total Taxes: $_____

Utilities

Phone: $_____   Internet: $_____

Electric: $_____   Television: $_____

Gas: $_____   Water/sewer: $_____

Trash collection: $_____   Other: $_____

Total Utilities: $_____

Total Forecasted Annual Expenses: $_____

Exercise 2.3: Living Expense Worksheet

In the previous exercise you worked your way through the different spending categories to forecast your annual expenses. Now it's time to stress test those estimates by tracking your *actual expenses* over the next several months. To do this, write down your monthly expenses using the sample format provided on the next page. Include each category listed in Exercise 2.2 when creating your worksheet.

Expenses	Jan	Feb	Mar	Apr	May	Jun	Jul	Aug	Sept	Oct	Nov	Dec	Total
Automobile													
Accessories													
Gas													
Maintenance													
Registration													
Repairs													
Other													
Child Expenses													
Allowance													
Activities													
Babysitting													
Child support													
Day care													
Other													

Exercise 2.4: Track Purchases Over $500

While completing your living expense worksheet in the previous exercise, you may have noticed that certain spending categories lend themselves to higher dollar amounts than others. It's these high-value categories where you'll now focus your attention. For the next three months, track every purchase that you make over $500. Write down how long you considered the purchase and if you discussed it with your spouse or partner. The goal is to see if your high-value purchases are impulse buys that can be avoided, or if they're necessary to further the success of your financial plan.

	Item 1	Item 2	Item 3
Description:	_____	_____	_____
Cost:	_____	_____	_____
Consideration time:	_____	_____	_____
Discussed with spouse?	_____	_____	_____
Date:	_____	_____	_____

	Item 4	Item 5	Item 6
Description:	_____	_____	_____
Cost:	_____	_____	_____
Consideration time:	_____	_____	_____
Discussed with spouse?	_____	_____	_____
Date:	_____	_____	_____

Exercise 2.5: Cash Flow Summary

On the following page you will compare your forecasted expenses with the amount that you actually spent. You do not need to wait a full twelve months to complete this exercise. Even a few months of data will allow you to see which categories are routinely over budget. You can then use this information to update your forecasted expenses for the next several months.

	Amount Budgeted	Amount Spent	% of Total Income	Over/Under Budget
Automobile				
Child Expenses				
Clothing				
Consumer Debt				
Dining				
Education				
Gifts				
Health Care				
Household				
Housing				
Insurance				
Memberships				
Professional Fees				
Recreation				
Taxes				
Utilities				

After completing the cash flow summary, if you were over budget, was it due to emergency expenses, impulse purchases, or lack of planning?

_____

_____

_____

_____

What can you change over the next six months to help you stay within your budget?

_____

_____

_____

_____

_____

Exercise 2.6: Calculate Your Savings Rate

Tracking your income and expenses is vital to your financial plan because it allows you to determine how much money you're saving on an annual basis. You will only be able to accomplish the goals that you detailed in Chapter 1 if you're saving a sufficient amount of your income. In this exercise you will calculate your current savings rate and learn what adjustments need to be made to reach your target savings rate.

Step 1: My annual income is $_____ (see exercise 2.1)

Step 2: My annual expenses are $_____ (see exercise 2.2)

Step 3: My annual savings is $_____ (step 1 minus step 2)

Step 4: Annual savings $_____ ÷ annual income $_____ = _____%

Step 5: Step 4 answer x 100 = current savings rate _____%

Step 6: My target savings rate is _____% (minimum of 10%)

Step 7: To achieve my target savings rate, I need to save an additional _____% of my income. (step 6 minus step 5)

For example, assume that your annual income is $80,000 and your annual expenses are $75,000. Your savings are therefore $5,000, and your savings rate is 6.25%. If your target savings rate is 10%, then you will need to save an additional 3.75% of your income, or $3,000 annually.

Average Savings Rate by Age

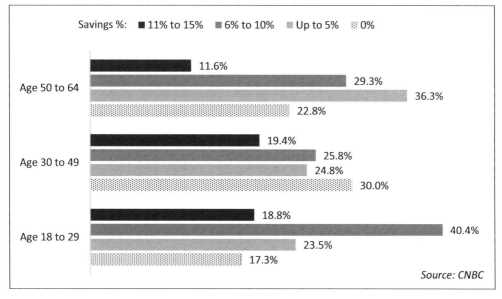

Source: CNBC

Now that you've calculated your savings rate percentage, don't be discouraged if it's not as high as you'd like it to be. By saving just a few extra dollars per week you can see significant gains over the long run due to the effects of compound interest.

Long-Term Effects of Increased Savings					
Monthly Savings	Value in 5 Years	Value in 10 Years	Value in 20 Years	Value in 30 Years	Value in 40 Years
$25	$1,835	$4,532	$14,317	$35,440	$81,045
$50	$3,671	$9,064	$28,633	$70,881	$162,091
$100	$7,341	$18,128	$57,266	$141,761	$324,180
$150	$11,012	$27,193	$85,899	$212,642	$486,271
$200	$14,683	$36,257	$114,532	$283,522	$648,360

✓ Assumes an 8% annual rate of return

CHAPTER 3

———————

Determine Your Net Worth

A safety net, or cash reserve, is a necessity for your financial plan. During your path to financial independence you're sure to hit some bumps in the road, and that's where your cash reserve comes in. The idea behind a cash reserve is simple. It's making sure that you have enough cash on hand to get you through difficult times. By building your cash reserve, you're providing yourself with a new set of options that you never knew were missing. You're giving yourself the option to wait for a better job, the option to retire early, and the option to spend more. Most importantly, you're giving yourself the option not to sacrifice your goals when the unexpected occurs.

Exercise 3.1: Cash Reserve Summary

Start by writing down your current cash reserve, which is commonly held in a checking account, savings account, money market fund, or certificate of deposit (CD). Do not include the value of your retirement accounts or other long-term investments when recording your cash reserve.

Bank: _____   Account balance: $_____

Account type: _____   Interest rate: _____

Exercise 3.2: Calculate Your Target Cash Reserve

Step 1: My annual expenses are $_____ (see exercise 2.2)

Step 2: My monthly expenses are $_____ (step 1 divided by 12)

Step 3: Minimum cash reserve: Monthly expenses $_____ x 3 = $_____

Step 4: Suggested cash reserve: Monthly expenses $_____ x 6 = $_____

For example, assume that your annual expenses are $75,000. Your monthly expenses are therefore $6,250. Your minimum cash reserve would be $18,750 and your suggested cash reserve is $37,500.

———————•—————

Now that you've calculated your target cash reserve range, is this amount sufficient to make you feel safe? If not, consider stretching your cash reserve to eight months or even one year. If you have two income earners in your household, then you may be able to reduce your cash reserve instead.

If you do not have a sufficient cash reserve currently saved, then your goal should be to increase your cash reserve to the desired level over the course of the next twelve months.

How does your savings account balance compare to your peers?						
Savings Account Balance	Age 18 to 24	Age 25 to 34	Age 35 to 44	Age 45 to 54	Age 55 to 64	Age 65+
$10,000 or more	7.5%	12.1%	16.0%	16.2%	16.8%	20.0%
$5,000 to $9,999	4.7%	5.4%	5.6%	5.2%	4.8%	4.7%
$1,000 to $4,999	14.7%	12.5%	9.8%	7.5%	8.0%	7.2%
Less than $1,000	19.1%	15.2%	11.6%	10.9%	10.7%	8.2%
$0	21.8%	26.3%	31.6%	30.8%	28.4%	27.6%
Min. balance only	9.7%	10.6%	6.6%	7.7%	8.4%	10.7%
No account	22.5%	17.9%	18.8%	21.7%	22.9%	21.6%
	100%	100%	100%	100%	100%	100%

Source: GoBankingRates.com

If you do not have a sufficient cash reserve today, describe what it will mean to you and your family to know that you are protected against unforeseen expenses.

_____

_____

_____

_____

Exercise 3.3: Real Estate Analysis

The next several exercises will be used to help you calculate your net worth. Although the calculation is straightforward (assets – liabilities = net worth), you will need to identify all of your underlying assets and liabilities which takes considerable effort and requires careful attention to detail. We start this process by reviewing your assets—specifically your real estate. Complete the summary below for all properties that you own.

	Property 1	**Property 2**
Description:	_____	_____
Owner:	_____	_____
Address:	_____	_____
Property type:	_____	_____
Date acquired:	_____	_____
Property tax:	_____	_____
Original cost:	_____	_____
Current value:	_____	_____

	Property 3	**Property 4**
Description:	_____	_____
Owner:	_____	_____
Address:	_____	_____
Property type:	_____	_____
Date acquired:	_____	_____
Property tax:	_____	_____
Original cost:	_____	_____
Current value:	_____	_____

The real estate summary that you completed captures your current financial snapshot, but what about your future? Perhaps you're renting an apartment and you'd like to someday purchase a home. Or maybe you're nearing retirement and considering downsizing to a condo or townhouse. There are a number of factors that you should consider when making the decision between buying or renting a home. A few of those factors are listed below.

Buying a home means...	Renting a home means...
Making a down payment	Making a security deposit
Monthly mortgage payment	Monthly rent payment
Paying property taxes	No property taxes
Homeowners insurance	Renters insurance
Paying for maintenance and repairs	Free maintenance and repairs
Potential to borrow through equity line	No potential to borrow
Tax deduction for mortgage interest	No mortgage interest deduction
Tax deduction for property taxes	No property tax deduction
Gain on home sale is excluded from taxes	No resale value

You should review the following questions with your spouse or partner before deciding to buy or rent a new home. If you're unsure how to answer these questions, review with your real estate agent and mortgage loan officer.

Question 1. Can you afford the mortgage?

Can you afford the monthly mortgage payment for a 15-year or 30-year fixed-rate mortgage? You should avoid adjustable-rate mortgages (ARMs) because the interest rate will change over the life of the mortgage depending on economic conditions. The problem with ARMs is that borrowers often don't know what their interest rate will adjust to until it's too late to lock in a better rate. ARMs were partially responsible for the 2008 housing crisis, because as interest rates adjusted higher, mortgage payments suddenly became too expensive, resulting in delinquent payments and foreclosures. Fixed-rate mortgages, on the other hand, are much safer because they allow borrowers to lock in interest rates that never change over the life of the mortgage. If you can't afford the monthly mortgage payment for a 15-year or 30-year fixed-rate mortgage, then you may need to rent.

Question 2. Can you afford the down payment?

Consider your ability to meet the down payment requirement. You should be prepared to put down at least 20% of the home's purchase price as a down payment. If you're applying for a jumbo loan (a mortgage exceeding $484,350 in most counties in the US in 2019), then you'll likely be required to put down 15%, 20%, or even 30% of the home's purchase price.

Location	Avg. 20% Down	Location	Avg. 20% Down
San Francisco, CA	$153,600	Phoenix, AZ	$42,060
Los Angeles, CA	$109,580	Philadelphia, PA	$40,360
San Diego, CA	$97,600	Las Vegas, NV	$38,920
Boston, MA	$76,220	Chicago, IL	$38,200
Seattle, WA	$71,880	Houston, TX	$33,400
Washington, D.C.	$71,060	Atlanta, GA	$32,800
Denver, CO	$62,760	Columbus, OH	$29,920
Portland, OR	$60,180	St. Louis, MO	$27,270
Baltimore, MD	$47,840	Indianapolis, IN	$25,700
Miami, FL	$44,680	Pittsburgh, PA	$25,080
Minneapolis, MN	$42,740	*National Average*	*$36,500*

Source: Forbes

Question 3. Are you prepared for the true cost of home ownership?

Make sure that you understand how expensive home ownership can be. According to mortgage firm Freddie Mac, homeowners on average will spend between 1% and 4% of a home's value each year on maintenance and repair costs.

Question 4. Have you considered non-financial factors, too?

- What's your commuting distance to work?
- What's the quality of the general public services in the community?
- Are there available recreation facilities nearby?
- What's the quality of the local public school system?
- What are the latest crime statistics for the community?
- What's the overall quality of life in the community?

Exercise 3.4: Auto and Vehicle Analysis

Next we'll focus on your autos and other vehicles, including boats, motorcycles, and aircrafts. Complete the summary that follows for all vehicles that you own.

	Vehicle 1	**Vehicle 2**
Vehicle type:	_____	_____
Owner:	_____	_____
Make/model:	_____	_____
Year:	_____	_____
VIN:	_____	_____
Title location:	_____	_____
Purchase date:	_____	_____
Original cost:	_____	_____
Current value:	_____	_____

	Vehicle 3	**Vehicle 4**
Vehicle type:	_____	_____
Owner:	_____	_____
Make/model:	_____	_____
Year:	_____	_____
VIN:	_____	_____
Title location:	_____	_____
Purchase date:	_____	_____
Original cost:	_____	_____
Current value:	_____	_____

Similar to the nuances of purchasing real estate, buying (or leasing) a new car also comes with a set of factors to consider. *Business Insider* highlights the key differences between the two options in the following chart.

Buying a Car	Leasing a Car
Requires more money up front, and each month.	Costs less up front and each month, so you can afford a more expensive car.
Can pay off your auto loan, which eliminates a monthly cost.	If you always lease, you'll make car payments for life.
Have the freedom to sell or trade the car at any time.	A lease contract is difficult and expensive to break.
Usually costs less than leasing overall, over time.	Can upgrade to the newest model every few years.
The car's value depreciates as soon as you drive it off the lot.	You'll owe fees for exceeding annual mileage limits or any damage to the car.

Consider the following questions before deciding to buy or lease a new car. Review with the car dealership if necessary.

Question 1. How many miles do you plan to drive?

Most car leases allow you to drive between 12,000 and 20,000 miles per year. If you exceed the limit, you'll be charged for each additional mile that you drive. The penalty for exceeding the mileage limit is typically $0.15 to $0.30 per additional mile, but varies depending on the lease. If you plan to drive your car more than the allotted number of miles, then you should consider buying.

Question 2. Is the lease ad misleading?

Be cautious of lease ads that offer unusually low mileage limits, such as 7,500 or 10,000 miles per year. Although your quoted monthly payment will be lower, you'll be faced with large penalties if you exceed the mileage limit, which cancels out the potential benefit. When deciding between buying or leasing a car, remember that the monthly payment alone is not always a good measure.

Question 3. Have you done your homework?

Before visiting the car dealership, make a list of the makes and models that you're interested in along with the features that you want. Be as specific as possible. Narrow down your search to a few cars, but don't have your heart set on just one. Finally, when you discuss price with the car dealer, ask for a firm quote in writing.

Exercise 3.5: Complete Asset Summaries

In this exercise you will complete summaries for your bank accounts, business interests, and other assets including antiques, art, collectibles, electronics, firearms, jewelry, etc. (Do not include your investment accounts or retirement accounts in this exercise. Those will be covered in detail later in this workbook.)

Bank Account Summary

	Account 1	Account 2	Account 3
Account owner:			
Bank:			
Account type:			
Account number:			
Account balance:			
Service fee:			
Interest rate:			
Phone number:			

	Account 4	Account 5	Account 6
Account owner:			
Bank:			
Account type:			
Account number:			
Account balance:			
Service fee:			
Interest rate:			
Phone number:			

Business Ownership Summary

Business name: _____   Business type: _____

Address: _____

Owner names and %: _____

Employer Identification Number (EIN): _____   Fiscal year end: _____

Annual revenue: $_____   Accounting method: _____

Total amount invested: $_____   Number of shares authorized: _____

Current value: $_____   Do you have an employment agreement? _____

Directors and officers: _____

Do you have a buy-sell agreement? _____   Do you offer fringe benefits? _____

Benefits provided: _____

Other Assets Summary (antiques, art, collectibles, electronics, firearms, jewelry, etc.)

	Asset 1	**Asset 2**	**Asset 3**
Description:	_____	_____	_____
Owner:	_____	_____	_____
Date acquired:	_____	_____	_____
Original cost:	_____	_____	_____
Current value:	_____	_____	_____

	Asset 4	**Asset 5**	**Asset 6**
Description:	_____	_____	_____
Owner:	_____	_____	_____
Date acquired:	_____	_____	_____
Original cost:	_____	_____	_____
Current value:	_____	_____	_____

	Asset 7	Asset 8	Asset 9
Description:	_____	_____	_____
Owner:	_____	_____	_____
Date acquired:	_____	_____	_____
Original cost:	_____	_____	_____
Current value:	_____	_____	_____

Exercise 3.6: Household Inventory

In the previous exercise you summarized the value of your assets, which includes the contents inside your home. However, mentally scanning each room and estimating the total value of your personal property is both inefficient and impractical. To adequately determine the value of the contents inside your home, you'll need to complete a household inventory. Although preparing your household inventory may appear to be an overwhelming task at first, it becomes much more manageable if you review one room at a time, and one category at a time. State Farm recommends that you inventory the following rooms by carefully detailing each of your possessions including the quantity, date acquired, original cost, and current value.

<u>**Rooms to Inventory**</u>
- Attic
- Basement
- Bathrooms
- Bedrooms
- Dining room
- Family room
- Garage
- Hallways
- Kitchen
- Laundry room
- Living room
- Office
- Shed/storage

<u>**Categories to Inventory**</u>
- Accessories
- Antiques
- Appliances
- Clothing
- Collectibles
- Electronics
- Fixtures
- Furniture
- Hobbies
- Jewelry
- Miscellaneous
- Precious metals
- Sports equipment

In the remainder of Chapter 3, we shift our focus from assets to liabilities. Any time we spend more money than we earn, we're probably making up the difference by going into debt. It's a common problem, but it's something that many of us know very little about. The upcoming exercises will teach you how much debt is *too much* and what strategies you should use to most efficiently pay off your debt.

Exercise 3.7: Real Estate Debt Analysis

As discussed earlier in this chapter, buying or renting a new home is a decision that has significant implications on your overall financial plan. Before obtaining a new mortgage, opening a home equity line of credit, or refinancing your current mortgage, review the information that follows, beginning with your housing debt ratio.

The relationship between your housing debt payments and your gross income is known as your *housing debt ratio*. Your housing debt payments (mortgage principal, mortgage interest, property taxes, and homeowners insurance) should not exceed 28% of your gross income.

For example, if your gross annual income is $50,000, then your housing payments should not exceed $14,000 per year or $1,167 per month. Now calculate your housing debt ratio by completing the following steps:

Step 1: My gross annual income is $_____ (see exercise 2.1)

Step 2: My gross annual income x 0.28 = $_____. This is the maximum
　　　　amount that I should spend each year on housing debt payments.

Complete the following summaries to determine how much you are currently spending on housing debt.

Mortgage Summary

	Mortgage 1	Mortgage 2
Address:	_____	_____
Borrower:	_____	_____
Lender:	_____	_____
Start date:	_____	_____
Initial balance:	_____	_____
Current balance:	_____	_____
Term of loan:	_____	_____

Interest rate: _____   _____

Fixed or variable? _____   _____

Monthly payment: _____   _____

Home Equity Loan Summary

	Equity Loan 1	**Equity Loan 2**
Address:	_____	_____
Borrower:	_____	_____
Lender:	_____	_____
Start date:	_____	_____
Initial balance:	_____	_____
Current balance:	_____	_____
Term of loan:	_____	_____
Interest rate:	_____	_____
Fixed or variable?	_____	_____
Monthly payment:	_____	_____

Home Equity Line of Credit Summary

	Equity Line 1	**Equity Line 2**
Address:	_____	_____
Borrower:	_____	_____
Lender:	_____	_____
Max credit line:	_____	_____
Current balance:	_____	_____
Interest rate:	_____	_____
Monthly payment:	_____	_____

Home Lease Summary

Address/property type: _____

Lessee: _____   Lessor: _____

Start date: _____   Term of lease: _____   Lease payment: $_____

Security deposit: $_____   Other fees: $_____   Renewal option? _____

Buyout option? _____   Buyout terms: _____

If you have found that you're dedicating too much money towards housing debt payments, one of the easiest solutions is to refinance your mortgage to a lower fixed rate. With interest rates being near all-time lows, there has never been a more attractive time to refinance. But beware: Not all refinancing options are created equal. To determine if refinancing is in your best interest, complete the following break-even analysis:

Refinance cost ÷ (current payment − new payment) = break even

For example, assume that you're refinancing your home that carries a 30-year mortgage with a balance of $200,000. Your current interest rate is 5.5% and your new interest rate will be 4.99%. Your current mortgage payment is $1,135.58 per month, and your new mortgage payment will be $1,072.42. The cost to refinance is $1,000.

$1,000 ÷ ($1,135.58 − $1,072.42) = 15.8 months to break even

Assuming the same scenario, if the cost to refinance your mortgage was increased to $4,000 would refinancing still be worthwhile? Probably not!

$4,000 ÷ ($1,135.58 − $1,072.42) = 63.3 months to break even

In general, if the break-even period is longer than the length of time that you plan to remain in your home, then refinancing is not recommended. The exception would be if you are refinancing from an adjustable-rate mortgage (ARM) to a fixed-rate mortgage. When refinancing from an ARM, the risk of rising interest rates may outweigh the increased length of time that it takes to break even.

15-Year vs 30-Year Mortgage

The refinancing examples provided above assume a 30-year mortgage. But what if the borrower had the ability to refinance from a 30-year to a 15-year mortgage? While the monthly payment will be higher with a 15-year mortgage, the total amount of interest that will be paid over the life of the loan will be far less. This principle is illustrated in the following tables.

Amount financed: $100,000 at 5% interest		
	30-year mortgage	**15-year mortgage**
Monthly principal + interest	$536.82	$790.79
Total monthly payments	$193,255.78	$142,342.85
Payment savings		$50,912.93

Amount financed: $200,000 at 5% interest		
	30-year mortgage	**15-year mortgage**
Monthly principal + interest	$1,073.64	$1,581.59
Total monthly payments	$386,511.57	$284,685.71
Payment savings		$101,825.86

Amount financed: $300,000 at 5% interest		
	30-year mortgage	**15-year mortgage**
Monthly principal + interest	$610.46	$2,372.38
Total monthly payments	$579,767.35	$427,028.56
Payment savings		$152,738.79

The Benefit of Making an Extra Mortgage Payment

What if you don't qualify to refinance your mortgage because your home value has decreased or your credit score is too low? If you find yourself in this situation, consider making an extra mortgage payment instead. By paying as little as $50 extra per month, you can significantly shorten the life of your mortgage. By paying an extra $300 per month, you can nearly cut the length of your mortgage in half!

Amount financed: $100,000 for 30 years			
Extra Monthly Payment	**Total Interest Savings**	**New Length of Loan**	**Total Time Saved**
$50	$18,534.09	24 yr 9 mo	5 yr 3 mo
$100	$30,579.21	21 yr 3 mo	8 yr 9 mo
$200	$45,546.73	16 yr 9 mo	13 yr 3 mo
$300	$54,593.27	13 yr 1 mo	16 yr 11 mo

Amount financed: $100,000 for 15 years			
Extra Monthly Payment	Total Interest Savings	New Length of Loan	Total Time Saved
$50	$3,965.75	13 yr 9 mo	1 yr 3 mo
$100	$7,236.62	12 yr 7 mo	2 yr 5 mo
$200	$12,318.30	11 yr 0 mo	4 yr 0 mo
$300	$16,095.53	9 yr 7 mo	5 yr 5 mo

Amount financed: $200,000 for 30 years			
Extra Monthly Payment	Total Interest Savings	New Length of Loan	Total Time Saved
$50	$20,776.37	27 yr 2 mo	2 yr 10 mo
$100	$37,068.19	24 yr 9 mo	5 yr 3 mo
$200	$61,158.43	21 yr 3 mo	8 yr 9 mo
$300	$78,256.11	18 yr 9 mo	11 yr 3 mo

Amount financed: $200,000 for 15 years			
Extra Monthly Payment	Total Interest Savings	New Length of Loan	Total Time Saved
$50	$4,168.31	14 yr 4 mo	0 yr 8 mo
$100	$7,931.51	13 yr 9 mo	1 yr 3 mo
$200	$14,473.25	12 yr 7 mo	2 yr 5 mo
$300	$19,963.45	11 yr 9 mo	3 yr 3 mo

Amount financed: $300,000 for 30 years			
Extra Monthly Payment	Total Interest Savings	New Length of Loan	Total Time Saved
$50	$21,656.77	28 yr 0 mo	2 yr 0 mo
$100	$39,934.86	26 yr 3 mo	3 yr 9 mo
$200	$69,203.71	23 yr 6 mo	6 yr 6 mo
$300	$91,737.64	21 yr 3 mo	8 yr 9 mo

Amount financed: $300,000 for 15 years			
Extra Monthly Payment	**Total Interest Savings**	**New Length of Loan**	**Total Time Saved**
$50	$4,234.94	14 yr 7 mo	0 yr 5 mo
$100	$8,191.86	14 yr 1 mo	0 yr 11 mo
$200	$15,365.89	13 yr 4 mo	1 yr 8 mo
$300	$21,709.87	12 yr 7 mo	2 yr 5 mo

After seeing the benefits of making an extra mortgage payment, list the ways that you could reduce your current spending or increase your income so that you can apply extra money towards your mortgage each month.

_____

_____

_____

_____

Exercise 3.8: Consumer Debt Analysis

Consumer debt includes credit cards, vehicle loans, and personal loans. Your total consumer debt payments should not exceed 20% of your net income. That is, the amount of income that remains after all taxes have been paid.

For example, if your gross annual income is $50,000 and you pay $15,000 in taxes, then your net income is $35,000. Therefore, your total consumer debt payments should not exceed $7,000 per year or $583 per month. Now calculate your consumer debt ratio by completing the following steps:

Step 1: My gross annual income is $_____ (see exercise 2.1)

Step 2: I pay $_____ per year in taxes (see exercise 2.2)

Step 3: My net annual income is $_____ (step 1 minus step 2)

Step 4: My net annual income x 0.20 = $_____. This is the maximum amount that I should spend each year on consumer debt payments.

Complete the following summaries to determine how much you are currently spending on consumer debt.

Vehicle Loan Summary

	Vehicle Loan 1	Vehicle Loan 2	Vehicle Loan 3
Description:	_____	_____	_____
Borrower:	_____	_____	_____
Lender:	_____	_____	_____
Start date:	_____	_____	_____
Initial balance:	_____	_____	_____
Current balance:	_____	_____	_____
Term of loan:	_____	_____	_____
Interest rate:	_____	_____	_____
Monthly payment:	_____	_____	_____

Vehicle Lease Summary

	Vehicle Lease 1	Vehicle Lease 2	Vehicle Lease 3
Description:	_____	_____	_____
Lessee:	_____	_____	_____
Lessor:	_____	_____	_____
Start date:	_____	_____	_____
Term of lease:	_____	_____	_____
Lease payment:	_____	_____	_____
Security deposit:	_____	_____	_____
Mileage limit:	_____	_____	_____
Buy-out option:	_____	_____	_____

Credit Card Summary

	Credit Card 1	Credit Card 2	Credit Card 3
Name on card:	_____	_____	_____
Creditor:	_____	_____	_____
Phone number:	_____	_____	_____
Account number:	_____	_____	_____
Credit limit:	_____	_____	_____
Expiration:	_____	_____	_____
Interest rate:	_____	_____	_____
Average balance:	_____	_____	_____
Min payment:	_____	_____	_____
Paid off monthly?	_____	_____	_____

	Credit Card 4	Credit Card 5	Credit Card 6
Name on card:	_____	_____	_____
Creditor:	_____	_____	_____
Phone number:	_____	_____	_____
Account number:	_____	_____	_____
Credit limit:	_____	_____	_____
Expiration:	_____	_____	_____
Interest rate:	_____	_____	_____
Average balance:	_____	_____	_____
Min payment:	_____	_____	_____
Paid off monthly?	_____	_____	_____

Student Loan Summary

	Student Loan 1	Student Loan 2	Student Loan 3
Description:	_____	_____	_____
Borrower:	_____	_____	_____
Lender:	_____	_____	_____
Start date:	_____	_____	_____
Initial balance:	_____	_____	_____
Current balance:	_____	_____	_____
Term of loan:	_____	_____	_____
Interest rate:	_____	_____	_____
Monthly payment:	_____	_____	_____

Retirement Plan Loan Summary

	Retirement Plan Loan 1	Retirement Plan Loan 2
Description:	_____	_____
Borrower:	_____	_____
Lender:	_____	_____
Start date:	_____	_____
Initial balance:	_____	_____
Current balance:	_____	_____
Term of loan:	_____	_____
Interest rate:	_____	_____
Fixed or variable?	_____	_____
Monthly payment:	_____	_____

Personal Loan Summary

	Personal Loan 1	**Personal Loan 2**	**Personal Loan 3**
Description:	_____	_____	_____
Borrower:	_____	_____	_____
Lender:	_____	_____	_____
Start date:	_____	_____	_____
Initial balance:	_____	_____	_____
Current balance:	_____	_____	_____
Term of loan:	_____	_____	_____
Interest rate:	_____	_____	_____
Monthly payment:	_____	_____	_____

Family Loan Summary

	Family Loan 1	**Family Loan 2**
Description:	_____	_____
Borrower:	_____	_____
Lender:	_____	_____
Start date:	_____	_____
Initial balance:	_____	_____
Current balance:	_____	_____
Term of loan:	_____	_____
Interest rate:	_____	_____
Fixed or variable?	_____	_____
Monthly payment:	_____	_____

Other Debts Summary

	Other Debt 1	**Other Debt 2**
Description:	_____	_____
Borrower:	_____	_____
Lender:	_____	_____
Start date:	_____	_____
Initial balance:	_____	_____
Current balance:	_____	_____
Term of loan:	_____	_____
Interest rate:	_____	_____
Fixed or variable?	_____	_____
Monthly payment:	_____	_____

	Other Debt 3	**Other Debt 4**
Description:	_____	_____
Borrower:	_____	_____
Lender:	_____	_____
Start date:	_____	_____
Initial balance:	_____	_____
Current balance:	_____	_____
Term of loan:	_____	_____
Interest rate:	_____	_____
Fixed or variable?	_____	_____
Monthly payment:	_____	_____

Exercise 3.9: Total Debt Analysis

Your total debt is the sum of your housing debt plus consumer debt. Your total debt payments should not exceed 36% of your gross income.

For example, if your gross annual income is $50,000, then your total debt payments should not exceed $18,000 per year or $1,500 per month. Now calculate your total debt ratio by completing the following steps:

Step 1: My gross annual income is $_____ (see exercise 2.1)

Step 2: My gross annual income x 0.36 = $_____. This is the maximum amount that I should spend each year on total debt payments.

Now that you've summarized your debt and completed the debt ratio analyses, determine if you have passed or failed each test. If you fail any of these tests, it's a clear indication that you need to adjust your income and expenses moving forward. Remember, if you continue to fail any of these tests in the years ahead, it's unlikely that you'll be able to accomplish the financial goals that you defined in Chapter 1.

	Max Payment	**My Payment**	**Pass / Fail**
Housing debt:	_____	_____	_____
Consumer debt:	_____	_____	_____
Total debt:	_____	_____	_____

If you failed the housing debt, consumer debt, or total debt test, write down the steps that you will take over the next six months to reduce your debt payments or increase your income.

_____

_____

_____

_____

_____

_____

Exercise 3.10: Calculate Your Net Worth

In this exercise you will calculate your net worth using the information collected in the previous exercises. For each category listed on the left, write down the current value of the asset and then subtract any associated debt. The remaining value is your net worth. You should revisit this exercise any time you experience a major life event, such as marriage, divorce, birth of a child, death of a family member, or job change.

	Current Value		**Debt**		**Net Worth**
Investment assets					
Annuities:	_____	–	_____	=	_____
College savings plans:	_____	–	_____	=	_____
Commodities:	_____	–	_____	=	_____
Retirement plans:	_____	–	_____	=	_____
Stock options:	_____	–	_____	=	_____
Taxable investments:	_____	–	_____	=	_____
Tax-free investments:	_____	–	_____	=	_____
Other assets					
Business property:	_____	–	_____	=	_____
Cash:	_____	–	_____	=	_____
Checking accounts:	_____	–	_____	=	_____
Insurance cash value:	_____	–	_____	=	_____
Personal property:	_____	–	_____	=	_____
Real estate:	_____	–	_____	=	_____
Savings accounts:	_____	–	_____	=	_____
Trust assets:	_____	–	_____	=	_____
Vehicles:	_____	–	_____	=	_____

	Current Value		Debt		Net Worth
Other:	_____	−	_____	=	_____
Other:	_____	−	_____	=	_____

Liabilities

			Debt		Net Worth
Credit cards:			_____	=	_____
Life insurance loans:			_____	=	_____
Personal debt:			_____	=	_____
Student loan debt:			_____	=	_____
Taxes owed:			_____	=	_____
Other:			_____	=	_____

Total Net Worth   _____

How does your net worth compare to your peers? Refer to the chart and then write down your net worth goal for one year, five years, and ten years from today.

Average Net Worth by Age	
Age	**Net Worth**
18 to 34	$6,676
35 to 44	$35,000
45 to 54	$84,542
55 to 64	$143,964
65 to 69	$194,226
70 and older	$181,078

Source: U.S. Census Bureau

My Net Worth Goal:

One year: $_____

Five years: $_____

Ten years: $_____

Exercise 3.11: Debt Management

By completing the previous exercise, you learned that your net worth is a function of two factors: What you own (assets) and what you owe (debt). In this exercise we'll review two debt management techniques and then you will develop a strategy to efficiently pay down your debt. But before we begin, consider the following questions:

When was the last time that you felt frustrated or angry at the amount of debt that you have? Explain the circumstance and how it made you feel.

_____

_____

_____

_____

_____

Now consider what it would mean to be debt free. What would you do with the extra money that is currently going towards debt repayment? How would your life change?

_____

_____

_____

_____

There are two common strategies used to pay down debt, and they are known as the *debt snowball* and the *debt avalanche*. Review each strategy and then decide which meets your personal needs the best.

The Debt Snowball

According to the debt snowball method, a debtor would pay off his or her debt with the smallest balance first, while making the minimum required payments on all remaining debt. As each small debt is eliminated, it frees up additional cash to apply towards the next largest debt. This helps build momentum, but it does not necessarily reduce the total amount of interest that you will pay.

Debt Snowball Example					
Debt Description	**Current Balance**	**Term Remaining**	**Interest Rate**	**Monthly Payment**	**Payoff Rank**
Visa card	$1,378	-	18.99%	$445	1
Boat loan	$2,560	19 months	2.00%	$155	2
Student loan	$9,890	33 months	6.80%	$244	3
American Express	$11,903	-	15.67%	$660	4
Car loan	$14,385	27 months	4.75%	$316	5
Home equity line	$30,440	-	3.99%	$355	6
Mortgage	$169,489	243 months	5.67%	$1,540	7

My Debt Snowball					
Debt Description	**Current Balance**	**Term Remaining**	**Interest Rate**	**Monthly Payment**	**Payoff Rank**

The Debt Avalanche

The alternative to the debt snowball method is the debt avalanche. According to this strategy, a debtor would pay off his or her debt that carries the highest interest rate first, while making the minimum required payments on all remaining debt. The benefit of the debt avalanche method is that it reduces the total amount of interest paid, but unlike the debt snowball method it may not yield immediate tangible results.

Debt Avalanche Example					
Debt Description	Current Balance	Term Remaining	Interest Rate	Monthly Payment	Payoff Rank
Visa card	$1,378	-	18.99%	$445	1
American Express	$11,903	-	15.67%	$660	2
Student loan	$9,890	33 months	6.80%	$244	3
Mortgage	$169,489	243 months	5.67%	$1,540	4
Car loan	$14,385	27 months	4.75%	$316	5
Home equity line	$30,440	-	3.99%	$355	6
Boat loan	$2,560	19 months	2.00%	$155	7

My Debt Avalanche					
Debt Description	Current Balance	Term Remaining	Interest Rate	Monthly Payment	Payoff Rank

Choosing which of these methods is right for you will depend on your goals and level of motivation. If small, quick wins will encourage you to pay off your debt more aggressively, then choose the debt snowball method. If you're interested in reducing the total amount of interest that will be paid over the life of your debt, then the debt avalanche method is preferred. Which option will you choose? Explain your decision.

_____

_____

_____

Exercise 3.12: Understanding Your Credit Report

The debt payoff strategy that you select will have a direct impact on your credit report and credit score. Your credit report is essentially a summary of your financial history. Lenders use your credit report to determine whether or not they will extend credit to you, and at what interest rate. Working alongside your credit report is your credit score. This three-digit number, typically between 350 and 850, quantifies your creditworthiness to lenders.

How is your credit score calculated?
- 35%: Payment history
- 30%: Amounts owed on credit and debt
- 15%: Length of credit history
- 10%: New credit
- 10%: Types of credit used

Credit Score Benchmarks
- 800 and higher: Excellent credit rating. 1% of consumers with a score of 800+ are likely to become delinquent debtors in the future.
- 740–799: Very good credit rating. 2% of consumers with a score of 740–799 are likely to become delinquent debtors in the future.
- 670–739: Good credit rating. 8% of consumers with a score of 670–739 are likely to become delinquent debtors in the future.
- 580–669: Fair credit rating. 27% of consumers with a score of 580–669 are likely to become delinquent debtors in the future.
- 579 or lower: Poor credit rating. 61% of consumers with a score of 579 or lower are likely to become delinquent debtors in the future.
- *Source: Experian*

To obtain a copy of your credit report and credit score, contact the three credit reporting bureaus directly. They are Experian, TransUnion, and Equifax. Although each bureau uses similar methods to determine your credit score, the formulas are slightly different so your credit score will vary by bureau.

Experian
www.experian.com
(888) 397-3742
Experian National Consumer Assistance Center
P.O. Box 4500
Allen, TX 75013

TransUnion
www.transunion.com
(800) 888-4213
TransUnion LLC
2 Baldwin Place
P.O. Box 1000
Chester, PA 19016

Equifax
www.equifax.com
(866) 640-2273
Equifax Credit Information Services, Inc.
P.O. Box 740241
Atlanta, GA 30374

Exercise 3.13: Review Your Credit Report

It's not uncommon to find mistakes while reviewing your credit report. Because creditors and lenders use the data in your report to determine whether or not they will lend you money, it's imperative that you verify all of the information is accurate. If you find an error, you need to immediately contact the credit bureau that issued the report. According to the Consumer Financial Protection Bureau, the most common errors that appear in credit reports are:

Identity errors
- Wrong name, phone number, or address is listed
- Accounts appear in your credit report that belong to another person
- Fraudulent accounts appear in your credit report as a result of identity theft

Incorrect reporting of account status
- Closed accounts are reported as open
- You are reported as the owner of an account, but you are an authorized user only
- Accounts are incorrectly reported as late or delinquent
- The date of last payment, date opened, or date of first delinquency is incorrect

Data management errors
- Incorrect information has been reinserted into your credit report after being fixed
- Information that should no longer be appearing in your credit report still appears
- The same account appears multiple times with different creditors listed

Balance errors
- Incorrect outstanding balance is listed
- Incorrect credit limit is listed

CHAPTER 4

Investments

In order to achieve your financial goals, you'll need to develop a personal investment plan tailored to your specific needs. The upcoming exercises will guide you through the process of investing and help you understand your tolerance for risk. But before we begin, you first need to answer one simple question: Are you a trader or an investor? Consider these factors before you answer: Traders react to short-term changes in the stock market while investors take advantage of long-term trends. Traders buy and sell stocks weekly, daily, or even hourly, while investors use buy-and-hold strategies that lead to investment gains over the long run. Unless you have extensive knowledge of the stock market and hours a day to devote to research, your safest play is to be an investor.

What Do You Need to Be a Successful Investor?
- The ability to take and manage risk
- The ability to control your emotions
- Access to accurate information
- Strong quantitative skills
- High level of organization
- *Source: TheStreet.com*

When deciding whether to purchase a specific investment, it's important to recognize that not all investments are created equal. For example, investments like stock options and real estate carry significantly more risk than government bonds and money market funds. Consider a triangle comprised of all possible investments. At the top of the triangle (the top 10%) are the most speculative investments, and at the base of the triangle (the bottom 60%) are defensive investments. All possible investments can be found along this continuum as demonstrated on the following page. How do your current investments compare to the suggested allocation outlined in the triangle? After completing the risk tolerance survey later in Exercise 4.1, revisit this diagram to determine what changes should be made to your investment portfolio.

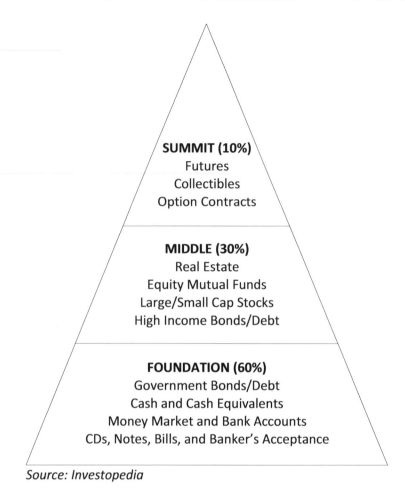

SUMMIT (10%)
Futures
Collectibles
Option Contracts

MIDDLE (30%)
Real Estate
Equity Mutual Funds
Large/Small Cap Stocks
High Income Bonds/Debt

FOUNDATION (60%)
Government Bonds/Debt
Cash and Cash Equivalents
Money Market and Bank Accounts
CDs, Notes, Bills, and Banker's Acceptance

Source: Investopedia

Exercise 4.1: Risk Tolerance Survey

When you think about investing, always keep the words "risk" and "return" in mind. The goal of investing is simple: Reduce the risk you're taking while increasing your investment return. But in order to do this, you first need to know exactly how much risk you're comfortable with. Answer the following questions to determine your risk tolerance.

1. How many years until you will begin making withdrawals from your investment accounts?

A. 2 years or less (1)
B. 3 to 6 years (2)
C. 7 to 11 years (3)
D. 12 to 15 years (4)
E. More than 15 years (5)

2. Once you begin making withdrawals from your investment accounts, how long will the withdrawals continue?

A. 2 years or less (1)
B. 3 to 6 years (2)
C. 7 to 11 years (3)
D. 12 to 15 years (4)
E. More than 15 years (5)

3. Which of the following portfolios are you most comfortable with? Assume $75,000 invested for 5 years.

	Worst Case	Best Case
Portfolio 1:	$70,000	$110,000
Portfolio 2:	$65,000	$130,000
Portfolio 3:	$60,000	$190,000
Portfolio 4:	$55,000	$200,000
Portfolio 5:	$50,000	$225,000

A. Portfolio 1 (1)
B. Portfolio 2 (2)
C. Portfolio 3 (3)
D. Portfolio 4 (4)
E. Portfolio 5 (5)

4. On January 1, 2018, you invested $50,000 in various stocks and mutual funds. On December 31, 2018, your account value is now $35,000. Which of the following describes the action that you would take?

A. Sell all of your investments (1)
B. Sell your riskiest investments only (2)
C. Compare your investment return to the overall stock market return (3)
D. Take no action today, wait and see if the investments recover (4)
E. Invest more aggressively to make up for the losses (5)

5. What is your rate of return objective for your investment accounts?

A. 4% or less (1)
B. 5% to 7% (2)
C. 8% to 10% (3)
D. 11% to 12% (4)
E. Over 12% (5)

6. When making a long-term investment, how long do you expect to keep your money invested?

A. 2 years or less (1)
B. 3 to 5 years (2)
C. 6 to 8 years (3)
D. 9 to 11 years (4)
E. More than 11 years (5)

7. How would you describe your level of confidence in managing your own investments?

A. Very confident (5)
B. Somewhat confident (4)
C. Confident (3)
D. Not sure (2)
E. Not confident (1)

8. If you unexpectedly received $50,000 *to invest,* which of the following describes the action that you would take?

A. Deposit the money in your checking or savings account (1)
B. Invest in CDs and government bonds (2)
C. Invest in large cap stocks and corporate bonds (3)
D. Invest in junk bonds and commodities (4)
E. Invest in stock options and artwork (5)

9. How would you describe your estimated income sources during retirement?

A. Very confident in my estimates (5)
B. Somewhat confident in my estimates (4)
C. Confident in my estimates (3)
D. Not sure (2)
E. Not confident in my estimates (1)

10. How would you describe your estimated expenses during retirement?

A. Very confident in my estimates (5)
B. Somewhat confident in my estimates (4)
C. Confident in my estimates (3)
D. Not sure (2)
E. Not confident in my estimates (1)

11. How much risk are you willing to tolerate in order to achieve higher investment returns?

A. I can tolerate a great deal of additional risk if necessary. (5)
B. I can tolerate some additional risk if necessary. (4)
C. I want to maintain my current risk level. (3)
D. I'm not sure. (2)
E. I want to reduce my overall level of risk even if it leads to lower investment returns. (1)

Evaluating Your Answers			
Combined Score	Target Allocation	% Invested in Stocks	% Invested in Bonds
44 to 55	90 / 10	90	10
29 to 43	70 / 30	70	30
11 to 28	50 / 50	50	50

The above chart shows the *maximum percent* that you should have invested in the stock market according to your risk tolerance results. The remaining amount should be allocated to fixed-income investments like bonds, CDs, and cash. Keep in mind, each investor is different and your present mood will affect your score. If you feel that your target allocation doesn't closely match your attitude toward investing, take the test again in a few days and compare your results. (Before purchasing specific investments you should review your risk tolerance results with a Certified Financial Planner. See the Epilogue for more details.)

Exercise 4.2: Understanding the Effect of Compound Interest

The final component of investing that you need to understand in order to become a successful investor is the powerful effect of compound interest. Very simply, compound interest means "interest growing on interest." It creates a snowball effect in your portfolio and its impact can be substantial over a long period of time. For example, if you were able to save $2,000 per month in an account that earns an 8% annual return, you would have well over $6 million dollars in forty years due to the effects of compound interest. By investing a total of $960,000 ($2,000 per month × 12 months × 40 years), your money would have multiplied nearly seven times to produce a final sum of $6,483,608.

A chart is provided on the following page to demonstrate the long-term effect that compound interest has on your investments.

Long-Term Effect of Compound Interest							
Monthly Savings	Value in 5 Years	Value in 10 Years	Value in 15 Years	Value in 20 Years	Value in 25 Years	Value in 30 Years	Value in 40 Years
$50	$3,671	$9,064	$16,989	$28,633	$45,742	$70,881	$162,091
$100	$7,341	$18,128	$33,978	$57,266	$91,484	$141,761	$324,180
$200	$14,683	$36,257	$67,956	$114,532	$182,968	$283,522	$648,360
$300	$22,024	$54,385	$101,934	$171,798	$274,452	$425,284	$972,542
$400	$29,366	$72,513	$135,911	$229,064	$365,936	$567,045	$1,296,721
$500	$36,707	$90,642	$169,889	$286,330	$457,420	$708,806	$1,620,902
$1,000	$73,414	$181,283	$339,778	$572,660	$914,839	$1,417,613	$3,241,804
$1,500	$110,121	$271,925	$509,668	$858,990	$1,372,259	$2,126,420	$4,862,706
$2,000	$146,828	$362,566	$679,557	$1,145,320	$1,829,679	$2,835,227	$6,483,608

✓ *Assumes an 8% annual rate of return*

When Will I Be a Millionaire?			
Monthly Contribution	You will have $1 million in...	Total Amount Contributed	Benefit of Compound Interest
$50	64 years	$38,400	$961,600
$100	55 years	$66,000	$934,000
$200	46 years	$110,400	$889,600
$300	41 years	$147,600	$852,400
$400	38 years	$182,400	$817,600
$500	35 years	$210,000	$790,000
$1,000	27 years	$324,000	$676,000
$1,500	23 years	$414,000	$586,000
$2,000	20 years	$480,000	$520,000

✓ *Assumes an 8% annual rate of return*

	Investing Now vs. Investing Later			
Year	Investor A's Contribution	Investor A's Account Value	Investor B's Contribution	Investor B's Account Value
1	$3,000	$3,240.00	$0	$0
2	$3,000	$6,739.20	$0	$0
3	$3,000	$10,518.34	$0	$0
4	$3,000	$14,599.80	$0	$0
5	$3,000	$19,007.79	$0	$0
6	$3,000	$23,768.41	$0	$0
7	$3,000	$28,909.88	$0	$0
8	$3,000	$34,462.67	$0	$0
9	$0	$37,219.69	$3,000	$3,240.00
10	$0	$40,197.26	$3,000	$6,739.20
11	$0	$43,413.04	$3,000	$10,518.34
12	$0	$46,886.09	$3,000	$14,599.80
13	$0	$50,636.97	$3,000	$19,007.79
14	$0	$54,687.93	$3,000	$23,768.41
15	$0	$59,062.97	$3,000	$28,909.88
16	$0	$63,788.00	$3,000	$34,462.67
17	$0	$68,891.04	$3,000	$40,459.69
18	$0	$74,402.33	$3,000	$46,936.46
19	$0	$80,354.51	$3,000	$53,931.38
20	$0	$86,782.87	$3,000	$61,485.89
21	$0	$93,725.50	$3,000	$69,644.76
22	$0	$101,223.54	$3,000	$78,456.34
23	$0	$109,321.43	$3,000	$87,972.85
24	$0	$118,067.14	$3,000	$98,250.68

✓ *Assumes an 8% annual rate of return*

➢ Investor A contributed $24,000 and A's account value is now $118,067.14.
➢ Investor B contributed $48,000 and B's account value is now $98,250.68.

Exercise 4.3: Complete Investment Summaries

To conclude Chapter 4, fill in the investment summaries provided. (Retirement accounts will be summarized in the following chapter.) Contact the brokerage house where your investments are held to obtain any missing information.

Taxable Account Summary

	Taxable Account 1	**Taxable Account 2**
Account name:	_____	_____
Account owner:	_____	_____
Account number:	_____	_____
Current value:	_____	_____
Cost basis:	_____	_____
Annual contribution:	_____	_____
Asset classes		
% Cash	_____	_____
% Bonds	_____	_____
% US stocks	_____	_____
% Int'l stocks	_____	_____
% Commodities	_____	_____
% Real estate	_____	_____

Tax-Free Account Summary

	Tax-Free Account 1	**Tax-Free Account 2**
Account name:	_____	_____
Account owner:	_____	_____
Account number:	_____	_____

Current value: _____ _____

Annual contribution: _____ _____

Asset classes

    % Cash _____ _____

    % Bonds _____ _____

    % US stocks _____ _____

    % Int'l stocks _____ _____

    % Commodities _____ _____

    % Real estate _____ _____

Stock Options Summary

	Stock Options 1	**Stock Options 2**
Owner:	_____	_____
Stock name:	_____	_____
Stock ticker:	_____	_____
Grant date:	_____	_____
Grant price:	_____	_____
Expiration date:	_____	_____
# Options granted:	_____	_____
# Options exercised:	_____	_____
# Options vested:	_____	_____
# Options not vested:	_____	_____
Pre-tax equity:	_____	_____
After-tax equity:	_____	_____

Qualified? (Yes/No) _____   _____

Asset class: _____   _____

Vesting schedule #: _____   _____

Vesting schedule 1: _____

Vesting schedule 2: _____

Vesting schedule 3: _____

Direct Investments Summary

	Direct Investment 1	**Direct Investment 2**	**Direct Investment 3**
Description:	_____	_____	_____
Owner:	_____	_____	_____
Purchase date:	_____	_____	_____
Original cost:	_____	_____	_____
Current value:	_____	_____	_____
Asset class:	_____	_____	_____

✓ *Direct investments may include oil and gas interests, commodities, limited partnerships, etc. where there is no additional layer of management between you and the investment.*

Rental Property Summary

Address: _____

Property type: _____   Owner: _____

Date acquired: _____   Original cost: $_____   Current value: $_____

Occupied? _____   Rental income: $_____   Operating costs: $_____

✓ *Operating costs include advertising, cleaning and maintenance, commissions, insurance, legal and professional fees, management fees, mortgage interest, repairs, supplies, taxes, utilities, and depreciation.*

CHAPTER 5

———•·•———

Retirement Planning

T his chapter will help you determine how prepared you are to meet the retirement goal that you defined in Chapter 1. You will also have the opportunity to revisit your original retirement goal and change it now that you've analyzed your financial data and developed a more comprehensive approach to managing your money. But before defining your specific retirement goals, let's explore your retirement expectations and concerns.

Exercise 5.1: Identify Your Retirement Expectations

For this exercise, place a check mark next to the retirement expectations that apply to you. Discuss these expectations with your spouse or partner.

_____ Living an active lifestyle

_____ Living a quiet lifestyle

_____ Spending more time with friends and family

_____ Working part time

_____ Volunteering and doing charity work

_____ Downsizing your home

_____ Relocating to a new city or state

_____ Traveling more

_____ Having less stress and living a simpler life

Exercise 5.2: Identify Your Retirement Concerns

Now that you've identified your retirement expectations, we will now explore your retirement concerns. For each item listed below, place a check mark beside the concerns that apply to you. Complete this exercise with your spouse or partner.

_____   Reduced income

_____   Outliving my money

_____   Low investment returns

_____   Declining health

_____   Rising costs of health care

_____   Providing care for a family member

_____   Becoming less active

Exercise 5.3: Establish Your Retirement Goal

You're learning that the idea of "retirement" can mean many things to many different people. The goal of this exercise is to determine what your ideal picture of retirement looks like, and then lay the foundation to help you achieve that vision. But first, let's revisit your original retirement goal from Chapter 1. Is your goal still practical? Are factors that you had not previously considered now influencing your decision? Update your retirement goal with the newfound knowledge that you have learned through the first four chapters. If you're having difficulty determining the appropriate age when you should retire, consider the following ages that Social Security has deemed "full retirement age."

Year of Birth	Full Retirement Age
1954 or earlier	66 years
1955	66 years, 2 months
1956	66 years, 4 months
1957	66 years, 6 months
1958	66 years, 8 months
1959	66 years, 10 months
1960 or later	67 years

What year would you like to retire? _____

How much will you spend during your first year of retirement? $_____

What state would you like to live in during retirement? _____

Exercise 5.4: Preparing for Retirement

There are two ways that you can save money for retirement—through taxable accounts (brokerage accounts, savings accounts, etc.) and through retirement accounts (401(k)s, IRAs, etc.). Taxable accounts are easier for most investors to understand because there is less tax code jargon and IRS rules associated with them. But unfortunately, saving money through taxable accounts alone probably won't be sufficient to reach your retirement goal. This is because part of the investment earnings in taxable accounts are taxed each year, which means less money in your accounts when you retire. Retirement accounts, on the other hand, provide tax-deferred growth, so your earnings grow tax-free each year until you begin making withdrawals.

The Power of Tax-Deferred Growth

Assume that two taxpayers are each in the 35% tax bracket. Taxpayer A purchases mutual funds valued at $10,000 in a taxable account. The funds earn an 8% annual return. However, 35% of that return is lost to short-term capital gains tax when she reallocates her investments at the end of the year, so her after-tax return is reduced to 5.2%. Taxpayer B also purchases mutual funds valued at $10,000, but in her 401(k) instead of a taxable account. The funds earn an 8% annual return. Taxpayer B does not pay short-term capital gains tax when she reallocates her investments. Therefore, her investment return remains 8%. If this trend continues, the difference in account values over time is significant.

	Taxpayer A *Net return of 5.2%*	Taxpayer B *Net return of 8%*
5 years	$12,885	$14,692
10 years	$16,602	$21,589
20 years	$27,562	$46,610
30 years	$45,759	$100,627
40 years	$75,968	$217,245
50 years	$126,121	$469,016

Saving Money Through an IRA

If you or your spouse have earned income this year, then you're eligible to contribute to an Individual Retirement Account (IRA). The two main types of IRAs are Traditional IRAs and Roth IRAs. You can open an IRA for free at most discount brokerage houses like TD Ameritrade, Fidelity, or Vanguard. Refer to the following chart to determine which type of IRA you should contribute to this year.

	Traditional IRA	**Roth IRA**
Eligibility	Must be under the age of 70 ½ to contribute. Annual contributions cannot exceed the amount of earned income.	Same as Traditional IRA.
Contribution Limit	$6,000 ($7,000 if age 50+) in 2019.	Same as Traditional IRA.
Tax Treatment	IRA contributions are tax deductible. Ordinary income tax is owed on withdrawals.	No tax deduction for contributions, but withdrawals are tax-free during retirement.
Withdrawal Rules	Withdrawals are penalty free beginning at age 59 ½. Account owner must begin taking required minimum distributions beginning at age 70 ½.	Withdrawals are penalty free *and tax-free* beginning at age 59 ½. There are no minimum distribution requirements for Roth IRAs.

Source: IRS

Roth IRAs provide tax-free growth, which is a distinct advantage over Traditional IRAs. To illustrate this point, assume that a taxpayer is in the 28% tax bracket and trying to decide between contributing to a Traditional IRA or Roth IRA. If she is able to contribute $5,000 per year and earn an 8% annual return, the difference in account values between the two options is significant.

	Traditional IRA *Balance after taxes*	**Roth IRA** *Tax-free balance*
5 years	$32,841	$33,578
10 years	$84,045	$87,656
20 years	$289,696	$315,012
30 years	$798,368	$904,717
40 years	$2,068,165	$2,434,259

Unfortunately, not everyone qualifies to contribute to a Roth IRA. Income restrictions apply, as shown in the following chart. If your modified adjusted gross income falls within the phase out range listed, consult your accountant to determine how much you are eligible to contribute.

2019 Roth IRA Income Limits		
Tax Filing Status	**Income Limit**	**Contribution Limit**
Married filing jointly	Less than $193,000	$6,000 ($7,000 if age 50+)
	$193,000 to $202,999	Contribution phases out
	$203,000 or more	Ineligible to contribute to Roth IRA, but can contribute to Traditional IRA
Married filing separately	$0	$6,000 ($7,000 if age 50+)
	$1 to $9,999	Contribution phases out
	$10,000 or more	Ineligible to contribute to Roth IRA, but can contribute to Traditional IRA
Single	Less than $122,000	$6,000 ($7,000 if age 50+)
	$122,000 to $136,999	Contribution phases out
	$137,000 or more	Ineligible to contribute to Roth IRA, but can contribute to Traditional IRA

Source: IRS

Average IRA Balance by Age					
Age	**IRA Balance**		**Age**	**IRA Balance**	
25 to 29	$12,537		45 to 49	$68,683	
30 to 34	$20,456		50 to 54	$91,976	
35 to 39	$33,784		55 to 59	$122,957	
40 to 44	$49,948		60 to 64	$165,139	

Source: USA Today

If you have an old retirement plan provided by a previous employer, you may be eligible to roll it over into an IRA. The benefit of rolling over your account into an IRA is the wide range of investment options available through most IRAs compared to employer-provided plans. Refer to the chart provided to determine eligibility.

	Rollover To			
	Roth IRA	**Traditional IRA**	**SIMPLE IRA**	**SEP IRA**
Roth IRA	Yes	No	No	No
Traditional IRA	Yes	Yes	No	Yes
SIMPLE IRA	Yes, after two years	Yes, after two years	Yes	Yes, after two years
SEP IRA	Yes	Yes	No	Yes
Governmental 457(b)	Yes	Yes	No	Yes
Qualified Plan (pre-tax)	Yes	Yes	No	Yes
403(b) (pre-tax)	Yes	Yes	No	Yes
Roth 401(k), 403(b), 457(b)	Yes	No	No	No

Source: IRS

Track 401(k) Rollovers

	Rollover 1	**Rollover 2**	**Rollover 3**
Employer name:	_____	_____	_____
Account type:	_____	_____	_____
Old account #:	_____	_____	_____
Rollover value:	_____	_____	_____
Rollover date:	_____	_____	_____
New account #:	_____	_____	_____

	Rollover 4	**Rollover 5**	**Rollover 6**
Employer name:	_____	_____	_____
Account type:	_____	_____	_____

Old account #: _____ _____ _____

Rollover value: _____ _____ _____

Rollover date: _____ _____ _____

New account #: _____ _____ _____

In addition to contributing to an IRA, the following contribution limits apply to employer-provided retirement plans for 2019:

- 401(k), 403(b), 457 elective deferral limit: $19,000
- 401(k), 403(b), 457 catch-up contribution limit (age 50+): $6,000
- SIMPLE Plan contribution limit: $13,000
- SIMPLE Plan catch-up contribution limit (age 50+): $3,000
- SEP Plan contribution limit: $56,000
- Defined benefit plan maximum benefit: $225,000

Exercise 5.5: Complete Retirement Account Summaries

Complete the retirement account summaries provided. These include employer-provided plans as well as IRAs. Contact the brokerage house where your accounts are held to obtain any missing information.

401(k) Summary

	401(k) Account 1	401(k) Account 2
Account name:	_____	_____
Account owner:	_____	_____
Account number:	_____	_____
Total account value:	_____	_____
Non-Roth value:	_____	_____
Roth value:	_____	_____
Your contributions		
Non-Roth annual:	_____	_____
Roth annual:	_____	_____

Employer contributions

    Match %:   _____   _____

    Employer limit: _____   _____

Asset classes

    % Cash   _____   _____

    % Bonds   _____   _____

    % US stocks   _____   _____

    % Int'l stocks   _____   _____

    % Commodities _____   _____

    % Real estate   _____   _____

Other Employer-Provided Retirement Plan Summary

	Account 1	**Account 2**
Account name:	_____	_____
Account owner:	_____	_____
Account number:	_____	_____
Total account value:	_____	_____
Non-Roth value:	_____	_____
Roth value:	_____	_____

Your contributions

    Non-Roth annual: _____   _____

    Roth annual: _____   _____

Employer contributions

    Match %:   _____   _____

    Employer limit: _____   _____

Asset classes

   % Cash   _____   _____

   % Bonds   _____   _____

   % US stocks   _____   _____

   % Int'l stocks _____   _____

   % Commodities _____   _____

   % Real estate   _____   _____

SEP Plan Summary

	SEP Plan 1	**SEP Plan 2**
Account name:	_____	_____
Account owner:	_____	_____
Account number:	_____	_____
Current value:	_____	_____
Annual contribution:	_____	_____

Asset classes

   % Cash   _____   _____

   % Bonds   _____   _____

   % US stocks   _____   _____

   % Int'l stocks _____   _____

   % Commodities _____   _____

   % Real estate   _____   _____

SIMPLE Plan Summary

	SIMPLE Plan 1	SIMPLE Plan 2
Account name:	_____	_____
Account owner:	_____	_____
Account number:	_____	_____
Current value:	_____	_____
Annual contribution:	_____	_____

Employer contributions

	SIMPLE Plan 1	SIMPLE Plan 2
3% match?	_____	_____
2% match?	_____	_____
No match?	_____	_____

Asset classes

	SIMPLE Plan 1	SIMPLE Plan 2
% Cash	_____	_____
% Bonds	_____	_____
% US stocks	_____	_____
% Int'l stocks	_____	_____
% Commodities	_____	_____
% Real estate	_____	_____

Traditional IRA Summary

	Traditional IRA 1	Traditional IRA 2
Account name:	_____	_____
Account owner:	_____	_____
Account number:	_____	_____
Current value:	_____	_____

Pre-tax value: _____ _____

After-tax value: _____ _____

Annual contribution: _____ _____

Asset classes

% Cash _____ _____

% Bonds _____ _____

% US stocks _____ _____

% Int'l stocks _____ _____

% Commodities _____ _____

% Real estate _____ _____

Roth IRA Summary

	Roth IRA 1	**Roth IRA 2**
Account name:	_____	_____
Account owner:	_____	_____
Account number:	_____	_____
Current value:	_____	_____
Annual contribution:	_____	_____

Asset classes

% Cash _____ _____

% Bonds _____ _____

% US stocks _____ _____

% Int'l stocks _____ _____

% Commodities _____ _____

% Real estate _____ _____

Annuity Summary

	Annuity 1	**Annuity 2**
Account name:	_____	_____
Account owner:	_____	_____
Account number:	_____	_____
Current value:	_____	_____
Pre-tax value:	_____	_____
After-tax value:	_____	_____
Annual contribution:	_____	_____
Asset classes		
% Cash	_____	_____
% Bonds	_____	_____
% US stocks	_____	_____
% Int'l stocks	_____	_____
% Commodities	_____	_____
% Real estate	_____	_____

Exercise 5.6: Complete Beneficiary Summary

For each account listed in the previous exercise, you should have named a beneficiary to receive the account proceeds after you die. You can refer to your original account application or contact the brokerage house where each account is held if you're unsure who you have named as beneficiary. Record the beneficiary information for each account in the summary provided.

	Account 1	**Account 2**	**Account 3**
Account name:	_____	_____	_____
Account owner:	_____	_____	_____

Account number: _____ _____ _____

Beneficiary: _____ _____ _____

Relationship: _____ _____ _____

Date of birth: _____ _____ _____

Social Security number: _____ _____ _____

Phone number: _____ _____ _____

Email address: _____ _____ _____

Primary or contingent: _____ _____ _____

Share %: _____ _____ _____

	Account 4	**Account 5**	**Account 6**
Account name:	_____	_____	_____
Account owner:	_____	_____	_____
Account number:	_____	_____	_____
Beneficiary:	_____	_____	_____
Relationship:	_____	_____	_____
Date of birth:	_____	_____	_____
Social Security number:	_____	_____	_____
Phone number:	_____	_____	_____
Email address:	_____	_____	_____
Primary or contingent:	_____	_____	_____
Share %:	_____	_____	_____

Exercise 5.7: Summarize Your Sources of Retirement Income

Complete the retirement income summaries provided. Include all of the sources of income that you expect to receive when you are retired.

Social Security Income Summary

	Social Security Income 1	Social Security Income 2
Income recipient:	_____	_____
Year income begins:	_____	_____
Year income ends:	_____	_____
Projected income:	_____	_____

Pension Income Summary

	Pension Income 1	Pension Income 2
Pension name:	_____	_____
Income recipient:	_____	_____
Year income begins:	_____	_____
Year income ends:	_____	_____
Projected income:	_____	_____
Will amount inflate?	_____	_____
Survivor benefit %:	_____	_____

Part-Time Employment Income Summary

	Part-Time Employment 1	Part-Time Employment 2
Employer:	_____	_____
Income recipient:	_____	_____
Year income begins:	_____	_____
Year income ends:	_____	_____

Projected income: _____   _____

Will amount inflate? _____   _____

Annuity Income Summary

	Annuity Income 1	**Annuity Income 2**
Annuity name:	_____	_____
Account number:	_____	_____
Annuity type:	_____	_____
Income recipient:	_____	_____
Year income begins:	_____	_____
Year income ends:	_____	_____
Current value:	_____	_____
Cost basis:	_____	_____
Projected income:	_____	_____
Will amount inflate?	_____	_____
Survivor benefit %:	_____	_____

Rental Property Income Summary

	Rental Property Income 1	**Rental Property Income 2**
Address:	_____	_____
Income recipient:	_____	_____
Year income begins:	_____	_____
Year income ends:	_____	_____
Projected income:	_____	_____
Will amount inflate?	_____	_____

Trust Income Summary

	Trust Income 1	Trust Income 2
Trust name:	_____	_____
Trust ID #:	_____	_____
Income recipient:	_____	_____
Year income begins:	_____	_____
Year income ends:	_____	_____
Projected income:	_____	_____
Will amount inflate?	_____	_____
Is income tax-free?	_____	_____

Exercise 5.8: Retirement Needs Analysis

Before we begin your retirement needs calculation, it's important to understand the main obstacle that you will be facing during retirement: Inflation. Since the Great Recession of 2008, inflation has been minimal which means the price of goods and services has remained relatively flat. In fact, inflation has averaged just 1.86% over the past ten years. But when inflation spikes, as it did during the 1970's when it averaged 7.36%, retirees living on fixed incomes were profoundly affected. To make sure that you will not be forced to return to work or move in with your children due to insufficient retirement funds, your retirement needs analysis will assume a 3% inflation rate, which is the long-term average from 1927 to 2018. The effects of 3% inflation are demonstrated in the following chart.

Living Expenses Today	Living Expenses in 10 Years	Living Expenses in 20 Years	Living Expenses in 30 Years
$40,000	$53,757	$72,244	$97,090
$60,000	$80,635	$108,367	$145,636
$80,000	$107,513	$144,489	$194,181
$100,000	$134,392	$180,611	$242,726

✓ Assumes 3% inflation rate

It's important to note that inflation will vary depending on your geographic location. Although it's likely that you're familiar with the cost of living in your home state, if you plan to relocate during retirement, then it's important that you take state-by-state inflation variances into account. To demonstrate this point, the Tax Foundation has released the following data to show how much $100 is worth in each state.

State	Value	State	Value	State	Value
Alabama	$109.41	Louisiana	$109.41	Ohio	$111.98
Alaska	$94.61	Maine	$102.99	Oklahoma	$110.99
Arizona	$103.73	Maryland	$90.66	Oregon	$101.01
Arkansas	$114.29	Massachusetts	$93.37	Pennsylvania	$101.83
California	$88.97	Michigan	$106.27	Rhode Island	$101.32
Colorado	$98.04	Minnesota	$102.46	South Carolina	$110.50
Connecticut	$91.91	Mississippi	$115.34	South Dakota	$113.64
Delaware	$98.14	Missouri	$111.86	Tennessee	$110.86
Florida	$100.91	Montana	$106.16	Texas	$103.52
Georgia	$108.70	Nebraska	$110.38	Utah	$103.09
Hawaii	$85.62	Nevada	$102.35	Vermont	$98.81
Idaho	$107.07	New Hampshire	$95.06	Virginia	$97.47
Illinois	$99.30	New Jersey	$87.34	Washington	$96.34
Indiana	$109.41	New Mexico	$105.26	Washington, D.C.	$84.67
Iowa	$110.74	New York	$86.43	West Virginia	$112.49
Kansas	$110.25	North Carolina	$109.05	Wisconsin	$107.07
Kentucky	$112.74	North Dakota	$109.29	Wyoming	$103.95

We're now ready to begin your retirement needs analysis. You'll be guided through a three-step process designed to calculate how much money you'll need to have by the time you retire. You should revisit this projection at least annually.

Step 1: Determine your annual income need during retirement.

Using the chart provided, find the amount of living expenses in the left-hand column that most closely matches how much you plan to spend (in today's dollars) each year during retirement. Then find the intersection of that dollar amount and the year that you plan to retire. For example, if you plan to spend $50,000 per year during retirement, and you would like to retire in 20 years, then you will be spending $90,305 during your first year of retirement. (Round to $90,000)

Expenses Today	Expenses in 5 Years	Expenses in 10 Years	Expenses in 15 Years	Expenses in 20 Years	Expenses in 25 Years	Expenses in 30 Years
$30,000	$34,778	$40,317	$46,739	$54,183	$62,813	$72,816
$40,000	$46,371	$53,757	$62,319	$72,244	$83,751	$97,091
$50,000	$57,964	$67,196	$77,898	$90,305	$104,689	$121,363
$60,000	$69,556	$80,635	$93,478	$108,367	$125,627	$145,636
$70,000	$81,149	$94,074	$109,058	$126,428	$146,564	$169,908
$80,000	$92,742	$107,513	$124,637	$144,489	$167,502	$194,181
$90,000	$104,335	$120,952	$140,217	$162,550	$188,440	$218,454
$100,000	$115,927	$134,392	$155,797	$180,611	$209,378	$242,726

✓ Assumes 3% inflation rate

My annual income need during the first year of retirement will be: $_____.

Step 2: Reduce your retirement income need by the amount of retirement income that you expect to receive.

For this step, be sure to include all of your sources of retirement income, including Social Security, pension benefits, annuity income, part-time employment income, etc. Use the amount that you expect to receive *during the first year that you are retired.* Refer to your account statements for projected income amounts.

Returning to our example, let's assume that you expect to receive $40,000 per year through various sources of retirement income, beginning the first year that you are retired. Subtracting that amount from your annual retirement income need found in Step 1, you're left with a remaining income need of $50,000.

$90,000 Annual retirement income need (step 1 answer)
– $40,000 Annual retirement income received
$50,000 Remaining annual income need

My remaining annual income need is: $_____.

Step 3: Convert your remaining annual income need into capital.

In our example, we determined that you will need $50,000 per year (in inflated future dollars) during the first year of retirement. Let's assume that you expect to live for 20 years after you retire. Using the table provided, you find that you will need between $661,502 and $913,715 in your investment portfolio by the time you retire. More reasonably, you could assume that an amount between $700,000 and $900,000 should be sufficient to retire comfortably.

Remaining Income Need	Length of Retirement	4% Return	6% Return	8% Return
$25,000	10 years	$239,455	$220,448	$203,853
$25,000	20 years	$456,857	$385,880	$330,751
$25,000	30 years	$654,237	$510,027	$409,744
$35,000	10 years	$335,238	$308,628	$285,395
$35,000	20 years	$639,600	$540,233	$463,052
$35,000	30 years	$915,932	$714,038	$573,642
$50,000	10 years	$478,911	$440,897	$407,707
$50,000	20 years	$913,715	$771,761	$661,502
$50,000	30 years	$1,308,474	$1,020,054	$819,488
$65,000	10 years	$622,584	$573,166	$530,019
$65,000	20 years	$1,187,829	$1,003,290	$859,952
$65,000	30 years	$1,701,017	$1,326,070	$1,065,334
$75,000	10 years	$718,366	$661,345	$611,560
$75,000	20 years	$1,370,572	$1,157,641	$992,263
$75,000	30 years	$1,962,711	$1,530,081	$1,229,232

I need to have between $_____ and $_____ saved in my investment portfolio by the time I retire.

If you find that you will need hundreds of thousands of additional dollars in order to retire, don't panic! Remember that you're making your first pass at your retirement projection, and your deficit will only get smaller as you continue using the principles provided in this workbook. To begin benchmarking your progress, use the chart on the following page to see how much you should have in total investments today, based on your current age and household income. Simply find the intersection of your age and income level, and then multiply by the factor provided. For example, if you are 35-years-old with a household income of $100,000, then you should have approximately $190,000 in total investments today ($100,000 × 1.9 = $190,000).

	$30,000	$50,000	$75,000	$100,000	$150,000	$200,000	$250,000
25	-	0.2	0.6	0.9	1.2	1.6	1.8
30	0.1	0.5	1.1	1.4	1.8	2.2	2.4
35	0.4	0.8	1.7	1.9	2.5	2.8	3.2
40	0.7	1.2	2.3	2.6	3.2	3.8	4.1
45	1.0	1.8	3.1	3.6	4.3	4.8	5.3
50	1.6	2.7	4.1	4.6	5.4	6.3	6.7
55	2.2	3.2	5.2	5.8	7.1	7.9	8.6
60	2.8	4.4	6.7	7.4	8.7	10.0	10.7
65	4.1	5.7	8.6	9.5	11.3	12.8	13.6

Step 1: My current age is: _____

Step 2: My household income is: $_____

Step 3: My investment factor is: _____

Step 4: I should have $_____ invested today (step 2 × step 3)

CHAPTER 6

———•—•———

Insurance

When you think about managing your money and creating a financial plan, you need to look beyond just investing and what's in your retirement accounts. Financial planning is a complete process, which means the stock market is just one piece of the puzzle. If your entire financial plan is based only on investing, there's no way you'll survive the next recession. It's during difficult times like these that a traffic accident, a house fire, or a medical crisis could devastate your financial plan if you're not careful. That's why you need to make sure that you have adequate insurance coverage that will protect you if an accident or loss occurs. You need to have the following lines of insurance, at a minimum, to protect yourself: auto, homeowners, health, disability, and possibly life insurance. There are money saving strategies that you can employ for each type if you know where to look and what questions to ask.

Exercise 6.1: Choosing an Insurance Provider

In this exercise, you will learn the factors needed to select an insurance company and evaluate their policies. There are six factors to consider when evaluating an insurance company and they are:

1. Adequacy of policy limits
2. Cost
3. Potential gaps in coverage
4. Quality of service
5. Company's financial stability
6. Company's claim settlement procedure

Ask your insurance agent to discuss each of these factors as a way to test his ability to effectively communicate with you. If your agent isn't willing to answer your questions now, just think how helpful he'll be when you need to file a claim!

Once you've found an insurance company that you're comfortable with, check with your state's insurance commissioner's office to see if they've received any recent customer complaints. For assistance locating your state's insurance commissioner visit The National Association of Insurance Commissioners at www.naic.org.

Exercise 6.2: Life Insurance Needs Analysis

Purchasing life insurance without a clear need for coverage is a common mistake that financial planners see many new clients make. In general, you only need life insurance if someone else is dependent on your income, you have a specific goal that you want to fund at death, or you want to provide enough money to pay for your burial costs. To calculate your need for life insurance, complete the following steps:

Step 1: Add together your estimated burial costs and any outstanding debts that you currently owe.

Step 2: Multiply the annual amount of income that your spouse and dependents will need by the number of years they will need the income. For example, if you want to provide your survivors with $20,000 per year for ten years, you would multiply these numbers together to get $200,000.

Step 3: Add the values from Step 1 and Step 2.

Step 4: Subtract your current available resources, including other life insurance coverage, that can quickly be converted to cash to help meet your survivors' income need. (Do not include your car, home, or similar assets if your survivors will need them after you die.) The result represents the amount of life insurance coverage that you should consider buying. Review this calculation with your insurance agent and make adjustments as needed.

Step 1: Final Expenses

Burial costs	$_____	
+ Debts owed	+ $_____	
Total final expenses		$_____

Step 2: Survivors' Income Need

Survivors' annual income need	$_____	
× Years to provide income	× _____	
Total survivors' income need		$_____

Step 3: Subtotal

Step 1 answer $ _____

+ Step 2 answer   + $_____

Subtotal $_____

Step 4: Life Insurance Needed

Step 3 answer $_____

– Available resources   – $_____

Life insurance needed $_____

After determining your need for life insurance, you'll next decide which type of policy is right for you. Consider the following differences between the two main types of life insurance—term and whole life—and discuss suitability with your insurance agent. Other types of life insurance are also available, including variable life insurance and universal life insurance, but these policies generally charge higher fees and act as a hybrid between life insurance and investments.

	Term Insurance	Whole Life Insurance
Duration	Policies are generally issued for periods of 5, 10, 15, or 20 years	Policies are issued for the insured's whole life
Death benefit	Death benefit will be paid if the insured dies during the term of the policy	Death benefit will be paid regardless of when death occurs
Cash value	None	Savings can accumulate within the policy
Borrowing from policy	Not permitted	Permitted, but subject to a specified interest rate
Cost of premiums	Relatively inexpensive	More expensive than term insurance
Tax advantages	None	Yes

Exercise 6.3: Complete Life Insurance Summaries

	Term Policy 1	**Term Policy 2**	**Term Policy 3**
Policy owner:	_____	_____	_____
Insured:	_____	_____	_____
Issuing company:	_____	_____	_____
Policy number:	_____	_____	_____
Face value:	_____	_____	_____
Policy issue date:	_____	_____	_____
Age at issue:	_____	_____	_____
Term length:	_____	_____	_____
Annual premium:	_____	_____	_____
Premium due date:	_____	_____	_____
Beneficiary:	_____	_____	_____
Policy rider 1:	_____	_____	_____
Policy rider 2:	_____	_____	_____
Agent name:	_____	_____	_____
Agent phone:	_____	_____	_____

	Whole Life Policy 1	**Whole Life Policy 2**	**Whole Life Policy 3**
Policy owner:	_____	_____	_____
Insured:	_____	_____	_____
Issuing company:	_____	_____	_____
Policy number:	_____	_____	_____
Face value:	_____	_____	_____
Death benefit:	_____	_____	_____

Cash value: _____ _____ _____

Surrender value: _____ _____ _____

Policy issue date: _____ _____ _____

Age at issue: _____ _____ _____

Annual premium: _____ _____ _____

Premium due date: _____ _____ _____

Beneficiary: _____ _____ _____

Dividend option: _____ _____ _____

Loan amount: _____ _____ _____

Loan interest: _____ _____ _____

Policy rider 1: _____ _____ _____

Policy rider 2: _____ _____ _____

Agent name: _____ _____ _____

Agent phone: _____ _____ _____

Exercise 6.4: Disability Insurance Needs Analysis

The average 30-year-old has a one in three chance of becoming disabled for more than 90 days before retirement. That's a sobering statistic. It means that between you, your spouse, and your siblings, the odds are overwhelming that at least one of you will face long-term disability before you retire. Being disabled means sacrifice, doctor bills, and having to make difficult personal decisions. Fortunately, disability insurance will provide you with income each year you're disabled so that you can begin living again. It's a necessity for your financial plan.

Each policy has its own definition of disability, and understanding that definition is critical to separate the good policies from the bad. There are three definitions of disability that you need to know, and they are:

1. Any occupation
2. Own occupation
3. Split definition

Definition 1: Any Occupation

The first definition of disability is known as "any occupation," and it's the least favorable definition for you and the best one for the insurance company. "Any occupation" means that if you become disabled, your policy will only provide benefits if you're unable to perform the duties of *any occupation*.

Definition 2: Own Occupation

The "own occupation" definition of disability is much better for you than the more liberal "any occupation" definition. "Own occupation" means that you will receive benefits if you become disabled and you're unable to perform the duties of your *own occupation* for which you were trained and educated. *For the safety of you and your financial plan, you should only consider policies that use the "own occupation" definition of disability.*

Definition 3: Split Definition

The third definition of disability is known as the "split definition" and it's commonly found in employer-provided disability policies. A policy with a split definition of disability will provide benefits if you become disabled and you're unable to perform the duties of your own occupation for a certain period of time (usually two years), and then it will provide benefits if you're unable to perform the duties of any occupation afterwards.

Exercise 6.5: Complete Disability Insurance Summary

	Disability Policy 1	**Disability Policy 2**
Policy owner:	_____	_____
Insured:	_____	_____
Issuing company:	_____	_____
Policy number:	_____	_____
Policy issue date:	_____	_____
Age at issue:	_____	_____
Annual premium:	_____	_____
Premium due date:	_____	_____

Monthly benefit: _____   _____

Elimination period: _____   _____

Payable to age: _____   _____

Disability definition: _____   _____

Policy rider 1: _____   _____

Policy rider 2: _____   _____

Policy rider 3: _____   _____

Agent name: _____   _____

Agent phone: _____   _____

Exercise 6.6: Health Insurance Analysis

You should never go without health insurance. Even if you're young and healthy, it's a risk you can't afford to take. Many different companies offer health insurance, and it can be difficult trying to select one. If you're in need of a referral, contact your local hospital, pharmacy, or clinic and ask what health insurance companies they recommend. Then call these companies and have them explain the different options available to you. You should consider health insurance plans that offer one or two free doctor visits each year along with a free annual checkup. Having prescription drug coverage is also important, but the more features you add, the more expensive your insurance premium will be.

Choosing a Health Insurance Deductible

One of the most important decisions that you'll need to make when it comes to your health insurance is deciding what your deductible should be. The lower your deductible, the higher your premium.

A useful strategy to select a health insurance deductible is to add up your medical expenses from the past three years and find the average amount that you spent per year. This average can be used as your current year deductible if you want to be aggressive and expect to have reduced medical expenses in the upcoming years. If you want to be more cautious, follow the same method, but divide your average expenses in half and make that your deductible instead.

Aggressive Strategy	Conservative Strategy
• 2016: $500 medical expenses	• 2016: $500 medical expenses
• 2017: $1,500 medical expenses	• 2017: $1,500 medical expenses
• 2018: $1,000 medical expenses	• 2018: $1,000 medical expenses
• Average = $1,000	• Average = $1,000
• Deductible = $1,000	• Deductible = $1,000 ÷ 2 = $500
• Result: Lower premium	• Result: Higher premium

Exercise 6.7: Complete Medical Insurance Summaries

Health Insurance Summary

Insured(s): _____

Insurance company: _____ Policy number: _____

Policy date: _____ Annual premium: $_____ Premium due date: _____

Network: _____ Co-insurance: _____%

Individual in-network deductible: $_____ Family in-network deductible: $_____

Individual out-of-pocket max: $_____ Family out-of-pocket max: $_____

Preventive care co-payment: $_____ Emergency room co-payment: $_____

Urgent care co-payment: $_____ Prescription drug co-payment: $_____

Other policy features: _____

Agent name: _____ Agent phone: _____

Dental Insurance Summary

Insured(s): _____

Insurance company: _____ Policy number: _____

Policy date: _____ Annual premium: $_____ Premium due date: _____

Network: _____ Co-insurance: _____%

Individual in-network deductible: $_____ Family in-network deductible: $_____

Individual out-of-pocket max: $_____   Family out-of-pocket max: $_____

Preventive care co-payment: $_____   Restorative care co-payment: $_____

Endodontic co-payment: $_____   Orthodontic co-payment: $_____

Other policy features: _____

Agent name: _____   Agent phone: _____

Vision Insurance Summary

Insured(s): _____

Insurance company: _____   Policy number: _____

Policy date: _____   Annual premium: $_____   Premium due date: _____

Network: _____   Co-insurance: _____%

Individual in-network deductible: $_____   Family in-network deductible: $_____

Individual out-of-pocket max: $_____   Family out-of-pocket max: $_____

Preventive care co-payment: $_____   Eyeglass frames co-payment: $_____

Contact lenses co-payment: $_____   LASIK procedure co-payment: $_____

Other policy features: _____

Agent name: _____   Agent phone: _____

Health Savings Account Summary

	Health Savings Account 1	Health Savings Account 2
Account name:	_____	_____
Account owner:	_____	_____
Account number:	_____	_____
Current value:	_____	_____
Annual contribution:	_____	_____

Asset classes

    % Cash   _____   _____

    % Bonds   _____   _____

    % US stocks   _____   _____

    % Int'l stocks   _____   _____

    % Commodities   _____   _____

    % Real estate   _____   _____

Long-Term Care Insurance Summary

	LTC Policy 1	**LTC Policy 2**
Insured(s):	_____	_____
Issuing company:	_____	_____
Policy number:	_____	_____
Policy date:	_____	_____
Age at issue:	_____	_____
Annual premium:	_____	_____
Premium due date:	_____	_____

Benefit limits

    Nursing home: _____   _____

    Home health care: _____   _____

Benefit period

    Nursing home: _____   _____

    Home health care: _____   _____

Elimination period

    Nursing home: _____   _____

    Home health care: _____   _____

Inflation provision: _____ _____

Qualification for benefits: _____ _____

Exclusion 1: _____ _____

Exclusion 2: _____ _____

Exclusion 3: _____ _____

Endorsement 1: _____ _____

Endorsement 2: _____ _____

Endorsement 3: _____ _____

Agent name: _____ _____

Agent phone: _____ _____

Exercise 6.8: Review Homeowners Insurance

The remainder of this chapter will focus on property and casualty insurance, which includes homeowners, auto, and umbrella coverage. Beginning with a review of your homeowners insurance, complete the following summary. Contact your insurance agent to locate any missing information.

Homeowners Insurance Summary

	Homeowners Policy 1	**Homeowners Policy 2**
Insured(s):	_____	_____
Issuing company:	_____	_____
Policy number:	_____	_____
Policy date:	_____	_____
Policy expiration:	_____	_____
Annual premium:	_____	_____
Premium due date:	_____	_____

Dwelling coverage: _____ _____

Other structures coverage: _____ _____

Personal property coverage

   Scheduled property: _____ _____

   Unscheduled property: _____ _____

Living expense coverage: _____ _____

Personal liability coverage: _____ _____

Medical expense coverage: _____ _____

Endorsement 1: _____ _____

Endorsement 2: _____ _____

Agent name: _____ _____

Agent phone: _____ _____

Each year when you receive your homeowners policy renewal notice, confirm that you are receiving all policy discounts that you are eligible for. Review the following list and discuss with your insurance agent.

Discount	**Do I Qualify?**		**Annual Savings**
Home security system	Yes	No	$_____
Smoke detectors	Yes	No	$_____
Living close to fire department	Yes	No	$_____
Within 1,000 ft. of fire hydrant	Yes	No	$_____
Being claim free	Yes	No	$_____
Multi-line discount	Yes	No	$_____
New home	Yes	No	$_____
Long-term customer	Yes	No	$_____

Exercise 6.9: Review Auto Insurance

Begin this exercise by completing the following auto insurance summary. Contact your insurance agent to locate any missing information.

	Auto Policy 1	**Auto Policy 2**
Insured(s):	_____	_____
Issuing company:	_____	_____
Policy number:	_____	_____
Policy date:	_____	_____
Policy expiration:	_____	_____
Annual premium:	_____	_____
Premium due date:	_____	_____
Comprehensive deductible:	_____	_____
Collision deductible:	_____	_____
Liability coverage:	_____	_____
Bodily injury per person:	_____	_____
Bodily injury per accident:	_____	_____
Property damage:	_____	_____
Medical payments:	_____	_____
Personal injury (PIP):	_____	_____
Uninsured motorist:	_____	_____
Bodily injury per person:	_____	_____
Bodily injury per accident:	_____	_____
Under insured motorist:	_____	_____
Bodily injury per person:	_____	_____
Bodily injury per accident:	_____	_____

Endorsement 1: _____   _____

Endorsement 2: _____   _____

Agent name: _____   _____

Agent phone: _____   _____

Each year when you receive your auto policy renewal notice, confirm that you are receiving all policy discounts that you are eligible for. Review the following list and discuss with your insurance agent.

Discount	Do I Qualify?		Annual Savings
Airbags	Yes	No	$_____
Daytime running lights	Yes	No	$_____
Anti-lock brakes	Yes	No	$_____
Anti-theft device	Yes	No	$_____
Being claim free	Yes	No	$_____
Multi-line discount	Yes	No	$_____
Multi-car discount	Yes	No	$_____
Favorable vehicle injury rating	Yes	No	$_____
Long-term customer	Yes	No	$_____
Driving low miles per year	Yes	No	$_____
Good student	Yes	No	$_____

Exercise 6.10: Review Umbrella Insurance

Umbrella insurance provides extra liability coverage above and beyond what is provided through your home and auto policies. It's designed to protect high net worth individuals (those with a net worth exceeding $1 million) from major claims and lawsuits that could otherwise leave them bankrupt. As a rule of thumb, the greater your personal wealth, the bigger your umbrella policy should be.

To better illustrate why umbrella insurance is needed, consider what would happen if you were the cause of an auto accident that led to $500,000 in bodily injuries to the other driver, but your auto policy only provided $200,000 of coverage. You could be held personally liable for the remaining $300,000. However, if you had acquired an umbrella policy with a $1 million coverage limit, then the umbrella coverage would begin where the auto policy left off, possibly saving you from bankruptcy.

If you were not familiar with umbrella insurance before this exercise, then review this coverage in detail with your insurance agent to determine if it's suitable for you. If you have already acquired this coverage, complete the summary below.

	Umbrella Policy 1	Umbrella Policy 2
Insured(s):	_____	_____
Issuing company:	_____	_____
Policy number:	_____	_____
Policy date:	_____	_____
Policy expiration:	_____	_____
Annual premium:	_____	_____
Premium due date:	_____	_____
Limits of liability		
Each occurrence:	_____	_____
Annual aggregate:	_____	_____
Required underlying limits		
Homeowners insurance:	_____	_____
Auto insurance:	_____	_____
Endorsement 1:	_____	_____
Endorsement 2:	_____	_____
Agent name:	_____	_____
Agent phone:	_____	_____

CHAPTER 7

———•———

Dependent Planning

For the purpose of this workbook, a dependent is any person that relies on you for financial support. Using this broad definition, a "dependent" can include a child, parent, sibling, etc. Summarize your dependents in the following exercise.

Exercise 7.1: Complete Dependent Summaries

	Dependent 1	**Dependent 2**
Name:	_____	_____
Relationship:	_____	_____
Home address:	_____	_____
Date of birth:	_____	_____
Social Security number:	_____	_____
Home phone:	_____	_____
Cell phone:	_____	_____
Email address:	_____	_____

	Dependent 3	**Dependent 4**
Name:	_____	_____
Relationship:	_____	_____
Home address:	_____	_____

Date of birth: _____   _____

Social Security number: _____   _____

Home phone: _____   _____

Cell phone: _____   _____

Email address: _____   _____

Exercise 7.2: Complete Dependent Account Summaries

Now that you've identified your dependents, summarize their associated accounts in the pages that follow. Contact the brokerage house where your investments are held to obtain any missing information.

529 Plan Summary

	529 Plan 1	**529 Plan 2**
Account name:	_____	_____
Account owner:	_____	_____
Account number:	_____	_____
Beneficiary:	_____	_____
Current value:	_____	_____
Annual contribution:	_____	_____
Asset classes		
% Cash	_____	_____
% Bonds	_____	_____
% US stocks	_____	_____
% Int'l stocks	_____	_____
% Commodities	_____	_____
% Real estate	_____	_____

Coverdell Education Savings Account Summary

	Coverdell ESA 1	Coverdell ESA 2
Account name:	_____	_____
Account owner:	_____	_____
Account number:	_____	_____
Beneficiary:	_____	_____
Current value:	_____	_____
Annual contribution:	_____	_____
Asset classes		
% Cash	_____	_____
% Bonds	_____	_____
% US stocks	_____	_____
% Int'l stocks	_____	_____
% Commodities	_____	_____
% Real estate	_____	_____

UGMA/UTMA Account Summary

	UGMA/UTMA Account 1	UGMA/UTMA Account 2
Account name:	_____	_____
Account owner:	_____	_____
Account number:	_____	_____
Beneficiary:	_____	_____
Current value:	_____	_____
Annual contribution:	_____	_____

Asset classes

% Cash   _____   _____

% Bonds   _____   _____

% US stocks   _____   _____

% Int'l stocks   _____   _____

% Commodities   _____   _____

% Real estate   _____   _____

Other Dependent Accounts Summary

	Account 1	**Account 2**
Account name:	_____	_____
Account owner:	_____	_____
Account number:	_____	_____
Beneficiary:	_____	_____
Current value:	_____	_____
Annual contribution:	_____	_____

Asset classes

% Cash   _____   _____

% Bonds   _____   _____

% US stocks   _____   _____

% Int'l stocks   _____   _____

% Commodities   _____   _____

% Real estate   _____   _____

Exercise 7.3: Teaching Early Money Lessons

As a parent, it's important to have open dialogue with your children about money and not be afraid to discuss your personal finances open and honestly. It's your responsibility to break the perpetual cycle of insufficient financial education being taught to children and young adults who then go on to make serious financial mistakes later in life. Until financial literacy is taught in schools and basic money management is included on standardized tests, the responsibility to teach these valuable lessons falls on you. To begin this process, review the following questions with your spouse or partner and write down your answers in the space provided.

What lessons about money did you learn from your parents?

_____

_____

What lessons about money do you hope to teach your children?

_____

_____

Growing up, was the subject of money rarely discussed in your household? Would you like to create a similar or different experience for your children?

_____

_____

If you taught your children lessons about money at a young age and raised them to become financially responsible adults, how might this provide you with peace of mind when you're retired?

_____

_____

If you pay your children an allowance for doing household chores, consider standardizing the process by using the worksheet provided on the following page. Share this worksheet with your children to show them the potential benefits of their hard work. Encourage them to respect their money by opening a savings account at your bank or credit union.

Allowance Worksheet								
Activity	**Fee**	**Mon**	**Tue**	**Wed**	**Thur**	**Fri**	**Sat**	**Sun**

Allowance Worksheet Example								
Activity	**Fee**	**Mon**	**Tue**	**Wed**	**Thur**	**Fri**	**Sat**	**Sun**
Clean bedroom	$2.00	✓						
Pull weeds	$3.00						✓	
Take out the trash	$1.00				✓			
Walk the dog	$1.00		✓					

Exercise 7.4: College Funding Analysis

The economic cost of being a parent has steadily increased over the last twenty years, now costing middle-income families nearly $250,000 to raise a child from birth to age 18. High-income families are now spending over $400,000 to raise a child, and these figures are expected to continue rising as the following chart demonstrates.

Cost to Raise a Child to Age 18			
Birth Year	**Low-Income Families**	**Middle-Income Families**	**High-Income Families**
1998	$164,385	$223,939	$326,840
2003	$164,956	$226,108	$330,786
2008	$172,979	$239,327	$396,725
2013	$176,550	$245,340	$407,820
2019 (Projected)	*$180,195*	*$251,504*	*$419,225*

Unfortunately, the figures do not include the additional cost of paying for your son or daughter to attend college. If you've decided that you would like to pay for your child's education, refer to the average college costs for 2019 that are shown below. Later in this exercise you will complete a college needs analysis to determine how much you will need to save each year to keep pace with the rising costs of college.

College Program	Annual Cost
Public in-state (4 years):	$24,061
Public out-of-state (4 years):	$38,544
Public in-state (2 years):	$17,000
Public out-of-state (2 years):	$27,923
Private (4 years):	$49,320

Now that you've seen the average cost to attend college, visit several school websites that your child is considering and record their costs below.

	College 1	**College 2**	**College 3**
College name:	_____	_____	_____
Website:	_____	_____	_____
Tuition:	_____	_____	_____
Today's date:	_____	_____	_____

	College 4	**College 5**	**College 6**
College name:	_____	_____	_____
Website:	_____	_____	_____
Tuition:	_____	_____	_____
Today's date:	_____	_____	_____

Use the following charts to determine how much you'll need to save each month to pay for your child's education. These figures assume that the annual cost is in today's dollars, your savings goal will be met by the time your child begins college, and college costs will increase by 5% per year while investments earn an after-tax annual return of 6%.

$24,061 Public In-State		
Years Until College	**Monthly Savings**	**Total College Cost**
17	$611	$237,696
16	$640	$226,377
15	$673	$215,597
14	$711	$205,331
13	$754	$195,553
12	$805	$186,241
11	$865	$177,372
10	$936	$168,926
9	$1,024	$160,882
8	$1,133	$153,221
7	$1,274	$145,925
6	$1,461	$138,976
5	$1,723	$132,358
4	$2,116	$126,055
3	$2,772	$120,053
2	$4,084	$114,336
1	$8,018	$108,891

$38,544 Public Out-of-State		
Years Until College	**Monthly Savings**	**Total College Cost**
17	$979	$380,772
16	$1,026	$362,640
15	$1,079	$345,371
14	$1,139	$328,925
13	$1,209	$313,262
12	$1,290	$298,345
11	$1,385	$284,138
10	$1,500	$270,607
9	$1,640	$257,721
8	$1,815	$245,449
7	$2,040	$233,761
6	$2,340	$222,629
5	$2,760	$212,028
4	$3,390	$201,931
3	$4,441	$192,316
2	$6,542	$183,158
1	$12,844	$174,436

$10,000 Tuition		
Years Until College	Monthly Savings	Total College Cost
17	$254	$98,789
16	$266	$94,085
15	$280	$89,604
14	$296	$85,338
13	$314	$81,274
12	$335	$77,404
11	$359	$73,718
10	$389	$70,207
9	$425	$66,864
8	$471	$63,680
7	$529	$60,648
6	$607	$57,760
5	$716	$55,009
4	$880	$52,390
3	$1,152	$49,895
2	$1,697	$47,519
1	$3,332	$45,256

Consider the following education incentives for 2019 to help offset the cost of college. In addition to these incentives, you should meet with the financial aid officer at the school your child will be attending to learn about all of your financial aid options. The officer should also help you determine if your child qualifies for federal student loans based on your income and asset values. For more information and financial aid eligibility, visit www.studentaid.ed.gov.

Lifetime Learning Credit
- The credit is equal to 20% of the first $10,000 of qualified education expenses.
- Modified AGI phase out for single taxpayers is $58,000 to $68,000.
- Modified AGI phase out for married filing jointly taxpayers is $116,000 to $136,000.

Coverdell Education Savings Account
- Maximum annual contribution is $2,000 per beneficiary.
- Modified AGI phase out for single taxpayers is $95,000 to $110,000.
- Modified AGI phase out for married filing jointly taxpayers is $190,000 to $220,000.

American Opportunity Credit
- The credit is equal to 100% of the first $2,000 of qualified education expenses, and 25% of the next $2,000 of qualified education expenses.

- Modified AGI phase out for single taxpayers is $80,000 to $90,000.
- Modified AGI phase out for married filing jointly taxpayers is $160,000 to $180,000.

529 Plan
- Maximum annual contribution is $15,000 per beneficiary.
- Up to five years of contributions may be gifted at one time, for a total of $75,000 per beneficiary.

CHAPTER 8

Estate Planning

Regardless of the size and complexity of your estate, you need to have a comprehensive estate plan in place to ensure that your assets will be transferred according to your wishes if you were to die, and that your healthcare wishes will be carried out if you were to become incapacitated.

Consider the following ten questions when developing your estate plan. Once you've established a comprehensive estate plan, review these questions annually with your attorney.

1. Do you have a will, living will, financial power of attorney, and healthcare power of attorney? Do you know what these documents are and why they are important?
2. Were your estate planning documents drafted or reviewed within the last two years?
3. Have you moved to a different state since your estate planning documents were drafted? Have they been updated based on the applicable laws of the state in which you now reside?
4. Are you working with a competent estate planning attorney whom you trust has your best interests in mind?
5. Do your heirs and other advisors know where your estate planning documents are located?
6. Do you have physical copies of all estate planning documents as well as password-protected digital backups?
7. Do your parents have a completed estate plan? Will you be expected to serve as their executor?
8. Have you and your attorney reviewed the state and federal estate taxes that would be due if you were to die this year?
9. Have you and your attorney reviewed all primary and contingent beneficiary designations for all of your accounts?
10. Have you and your attorney reviewed your assets (home, auto, personal property, and bank accounts) to ensure they are property titled?

Exercise 8.1: Complete Estate Plan Summaries

Complete the following summaries for your estate planning documents. If you do not currently have these documents or would like to discuss their suitability, consult an estate planning attorney. If you're unable to find an attorney referral through a trusted friend, relative, or business associate, then contact a Certified Financial Planner in your area (www.cfp.net/search) and request an attorney referral.

Will Summary

	Will 1	Will 2
Name:	_____	_____
Date signed:	_____	_____
Executor:	_____	_____
Contingent executor:	_____	_____
Guardian:	_____	_____
Distribution clause:	_____	_____
Specific assets clause:	_____	_____
Remainder clause:	_____	_____
Location of will:	_____	_____
Drafting attorney:	_____	_____
Date last reviewed:	_____	_____

Financial Power of Attorney Summary

	Financial POA 1	Financial POA 2
Name:	_____	_____
Date signed:	_____	_____
Agent:	_____	_____
Agent phone:	_____	_____

Alternate agent: _____ _____

Alternate agent phone: _____ _____

Location of document: _____ _____

Drafting attorney: _____ _____

Date last reviewed: _____ _____

Healthcare Power of Attorney Summary

	Healthcare POA 1	**Healthcare POA 2**
Name:	_____	_____
Date signed:	_____	_____
Agent:	_____	_____
Agent phone:	_____	_____
Alternate agent:	_____	_____
Alternate agent phone:	_____	_____
Location of document:	_____	_____
Drafting attorney:	_____	_____
Date last reviewed:	_____	_____

Living Will Summary

	Living Will 1	**Living Will 2**
Name:	_____	_____
Date signed:	_____	_____
Contact:	_____	_____
Contact phone:	_____	_____
Alternate contact:	_____	_____

Alternate contact phone: _____   _____

Location of document: _____   _____

Drafting attorney: _____   _____

Date last reviewed: _____   _____

Trust Summary

	Trust 1	**Trust 2**
Trust name:	_____	_____
Trust ID number:	_____	_____
Date signed:	_____	_____
Purpose of trust:	_____	_____
Grantor:	_____	_____
Trustee(s):	_____	_____
Successor trustee(s):	_____	_____
Beneficiary 1:	_____	_____
Beneficiary 2:	_____	_____
Beneficiary 3:	_____	_____
Is the trust revocable?	_____	_____
Location of document:	_____	_____
Drafting attorney:	_____	_____
Date last reviewed:	_____	_____

Exercise 8.2: Draft Letter of Last Instructions

In addition to the other estate documents already listed, you should also draft a Letter of Last Instructions. This letter is an informal document that provides survivors with information concerning your personal matters that will require immediate attention after death. A Letter of Last Instructions *is not* a substitute for a will.

If you've ever had a loved one die without having this information readily available, then you know firsthand how challenging it can be to make decisions during that difficult time. Please sit down with your family and discuss these matters.

Letter of Last Instructions Worksheet

Your name: _____ Today's date: _____

1. Notify the following family members and acquaintances

    Name: _____ Relationship: _____

    Address:_____ Phone: _____

    Name: _____ Relationship: _____

    Address:_____ Phone: _____

    Name: _____ Relationship: _____

    Address:_____ Phone: _____

    Name: _____ Relationship: _____

    Address:_____ Phone: _____

2. Notify my employer

    Name: _____ Phone: _____

3. Notify my attorney

    Name: _____ Phone: _____

4. Location of important financial papers and passwords:

_____

_____

5. Location of safe deposit box:

_____

6. Make arrangements with funeral home

Name: _____   Phone: _____

Organ donations: _____   Embalming? _____

Autopsy if requested by family? _____   Public viewing? _____

Type of service: _____

Location of service: _____

Dispose of remains as follows: _____

_____

7. Request 10 copies of the death certificate. (The funeral director can request these.)

8. Provide obituary

Name: _____   Phone: _____

9. Retrieve and process life insurance policies

Insurance company: _____   Policy number: _____

Agent name: _____   Agent phone: _____

Insurance company: _____   Policy number: _____

Agent name: _____   Agent phone: _____

Insurance company: _____   Policy number: _____

Agent name: _____   Agent phone: _____

10. Notify Social Security office

Name: _____   Phone: _____

11. Notify the bank that holds home mortgage

Name: _____   Phone: _____

12. Special wishes:

_____

_____

_____

_____

EPILOGUE

---·•·---

Your Next Steps

Congratulations! By completing this workbook you now have all the tools you need to take charge of your financial life. You've been introduced to the practice of personal financial planning and learned how to create and monitor a successful financial plan. You set specific and achievable financial goals and learned how to apply economic analysis to all financial decisions.

Although managing your financial plan can easily become an overwhelming experience, if you break down the planning process into the steps outlined in this book, it becomes much more manageable. Remember to stay patient, live within your means, and increase your financial IQ whenever possible. Please take a moment and reflect on what you've learned by answering the following questions.

After completing this workbook, what is the most important lesson you've learned that will change how you manage your money in the future?

_____

_____

_____

What did you learn in this workbook that you wish you had learned earlier? How will this new information impact your life?

_____

_____

_____

As you begin implementing the strategies discussed in this workbook, who will you rely on for additional coaching and assistance?

_____

_____

_____

If you decide to hire a financial planner to help implement the strategies outlined in this workbook, what do you expect him or her to help you accomplish over the next twelve months?

_____

_____

_____

Hiring a Financial Planner

A competent financial planner can provide you with peace of mind as you continue to develop your financial plan. Unfortunately, anybody can hang a shingle and declare himself a financial planner today. Industry regulations are lax, which means that you need to know how to protect yourself and find a planner that you can trust. That should go without saying, but in the post-Bernie Madoff era we live in, it can't be stressed enough. You can search for a Certified Financial Planner in your area by visiting www.cfp.net/search, but even then, you'll need to do careful screening to make sure he or she is affordable and able to meet your needs. Use the following questions provided by the National Association of Personal Financial Advisors (NAPFA) to interview potential planners and compare their qualifications and background.

1. What is your educational background?
   a. College degree
   b. Graduate degree
2. What are your financial planning credentials, designations, and affiliations?
3. How long have you been a Certified Financial Planner?
   a. 1 to 4 years
   b. 5 to 9 years
   c. 10 or more years
4. Will you provide references from other professionals?
5. Have you ever been cited by a professional or regulatory body for disciplinary actions?

6. How many clients do you work with?
7. How many meetings will we have per year?
8. What is your method of providing service?
   a. Do you provide a written analysis?
   b. Do you provide recommendations?
   c. Do you assist with the implementation of recommendations?
   d. Do you provide ongoing advice?
9. How is your firm compensated and how is your compensation calculated?
   a. Fee-only
   b. Commissions
   c. Fee + commissions
10. Do you charge a minimum fee?
11. Are there any incentives for you to recommend certain financial products?
12. Do you have a business continuity plan?
13. Will you sign a fiduciary oath?
14. Will you or an associate work with me? (If an associate will be your primary contact, have the associate answer questions 1 – 13.)

Evaluating Potential Financial Planners

Rate from 1 to 10

	Interview 1	Interview 2	Interview 3
Company:	_____	_____	_____
Impression of website:	_____	_____	_____
First interaction with firm:	_____	_____	_____
First interaction with planner:	_____	_____	_____
Impression of office setting:	_____	_____	_____
Impression of office staff:	_____	_____	_____
Consultation meeting:	_____	_____	_____
Planner qualifications:	_____	_____	_____
Fees:	_____	_____	_____

Once you've found a financial planner that you're comfortable with, make sure that he or she remains committed to your financial success for more than just the first few meetings. Your financial planner should act as a fiduciary by constantly reviewing your financial plan and implementing strategies that reflect your unique personality, lifestyle, and goals. To ensure that your financial planner is engaged in continuous financial planning, complete the following summary to document your ongoing communication.

Summary of Communication with Your Financial Planner

Date: _____   Contact initiated by: _____

Purpose: _____

Next steps: _____

Date: _____   Contact initiated by: _____

Purpose: _____

Next steps: _____

Date: _____   Contact initiated by: _____

Purpose: _____

Next steps: _____

Date: _____   Contact initiated by: _____

Purpose: _____

Next steps: _____

Date: _____   Contact initiated by: _____

Purpose: _____

Next steps: _____

ABOUT THE AUTHORS

Matt Brandeburg, CFP®

Matt is a Certified Financial Planner in Columbus, Ohio. He serves as the Chief Operating Officer for a fee-only financial planning firm with over $700 million in assets under management and he's an active member of the National Association of Personal Financial Advisors (NAPFA). Matt is the author of the books *Financial Planning For Your First Job*, *Your Guide to the CFP Certification Exam*, and *CFP Certification Exam Practice Question Workbook*. In addition, he teaches the class *Financial Planning in your 20s and 30s* at Ohio State University.

Sameer Khan, MBA

Sameer is a Manager in Deloitte's Financial Integrity practice, based out of New York City. Sameer's skills are deeply rooted in Finance & Accounting—Financial Planning and Analysis, Financial Reporting, Financial Close, Overhead Management, and Allocation Development. Sameer's expertise lies in supporting clients with business transformations across all finance and accounting related processes.

Aneeqah Ahmed

Aneeqah is a financial services professional in Columbus, Ohio, who has formerly served as head of data management and marketing for a fee-only financial planning firm with over $500 million in assets under management. Aneeqah has a strong background in cash flow management, debt reduction strategies, and retirement planning, and she has served as writer and editor for *Alger Magazine* while studying Finance and English Literature at The Ohio State University.

INDEX

38914809R00075

Made in the USA
San Bernardino, CA
15 June 2019